To Kimbe
Enjoy
Ernestine Townsend

MW00938983

A CENTURY OF STORIES

A CENTURY OF STORIES

Ernestine Townsend

Library of Congress Number: 2001116886
ISBN #: Softcover 0-7388-5707-6

This book was printed in the United States of America.

To order additional copies of this book, contact:
Xlibris Corporation
1-888-7-XLIBRIS
www.Xlibris.com
Orders@Xlibris.com

Contents

DEDICATION

To my loving family and friends who have long tolerated my passion for writing.
To my granddaughter Kathryn who asked me to tell her some stories.
And, especially to her grandfather who doesn't complain when he sometimes has to get his own lunch.

ELDORADO

ELDORADO

In 1870, my great grandparents, Eliza and Willard T. Farnham moved west from Ohio to southwest Iowa with their two sons and two daughters who were in their teens. They first built a rustic log cabin, and enjoyed rural life. In 1872, he superintended the erection of the beautiful residence. A lithographic view of the estate was displayed in the Iowa state atlas and was exhibited at the exposition in Philadelphia during the Centennial Year (1900). The artist named it "Eldorado".

Eldorado is defined as "A legendary kingdom sought after by 16th century explorers". During the development of the west and the gold rush days, it was used to describe a place of fabulous wealth or opportunity.

They lived there until they moved to Lake Elsinore, California in 1890. Their daughter, Ernestine, married Levi Baker in 1873, and lived at Eldorado until 1914 when their son, Eugene married Helen Gass. Eugene and Helen lived there until 1922, had three children and moved to a new home built on the Baker homestead a mile and a half closer to Shenandoah. Thaddeus and Donald (Thad and Don) were two and four years old when I was born during a blizzard on January 19, 1920. Four generations lived at Eldorado. This is where it all began for me.

This book contains many stories about the 20th century. For more about Eldorado, and the lives of the Farnhams, plus other stories of the 18th and 19th centuries, read "Other Centuries; Other Stories".

In 1972, just 100 years later, Dick and Dixie Fishbaugh built the new, beautiful home above on the same spot.

They wanted to restore the old mansion, but it was too deteriorated to be practical, so acting as his own contractor, he drew up new plans, blending the old with the new. Dixie, an especially good cook, loves her beautiful big kitchen (13 feet wide by 30 feet long) with a brick fireplace at one end. Dick designed and built the beautiful cook center and the fireplace with bricks from the old streets of Shenandoah. The kitchen also has a large butcher block from an old meat store. The ceiling is decorated with beams from the old house. In the living room, the newel post, stairway banister and balusters restored from the Farnham house lend a warm antique touch.

White corn and soybeans are the crops harvested. There are a few black walnut and fruit trees. Dick tends the grounds, the beautiful landscaping and the Cana flower beds. They make apple cider the old-fashioned way with a hand press. Occasionally, they enjoy a ride in their traditional sled during the winter, and the buggy on special occasions during warmer weather.

He discovered a limestone block that was used to step down on when unloading and loading the stage coach that used the Farnham place as a stop.

Now, we are corresponding by e-mail. That is what this book is about—life from the 19th century through the 20th century told in stories.

INTRODUCTION

Life is like a road map, constantly being unfolded. Sometimes detours aren't marked on the map. When you pass through one area, you have to unfold another map to explore new territory. And, like maps, you can't always get it back the way it was before.

This collection of stories about and by people who lived in the 20th century may bring back many memories to seniors, their children and grandchildren. To those growing up in the new century, perhaps some of the stories will be shared in their history classes.

Each person is born on a specific date, in a certain era, to particular parents, at a geographic location, under certain monetary conditions and type of government. You belong to this special family with certain traditions and family values, good or bad. The first years of your life are spent learning to live within this restricted and structured or unstructured situation.

Starting school, fitting these family values into the outside world becomes a challenge. This is what growing up is all about. You will constantly have ideas about doing things differently and better, but are told to wait until you are grown up.

As a young adult you are finally in charge of your life and can make these changes. But, you soon find this requires extreme dedication, effort, decisions, responsibility and positive action. Things don't change just because you want them to change.

When you marry, you have to blend two different sets of family values and traditions. Your children spend their first few years learning your rules and regulations. When they are grown and establish their own set of family values, based on their peers, their times, and their goals, the cycle starts all over.

In your later years, living in your children's and grandchildren's world, you may see a pattern of good values passed down from generation to generation. If you look closely, you may even see a few of your own traditions woven into the new.

As we enter the twenty-first century, transportation and communications are changing our world. New values and traditions will emerge. Hopefully new family values will be structured to better our world. This collection of stories will take you from the late 1800's to the new millennium. I will leave it to others to write stories of the 21st century?

The reader may find some words in this book that are now considered "politically incorrect", but are intended to illustrate how it was during that era; not to offend.

The brief genealogy information is just to help identify the people in the stories. Other members of the family are doing sophisticated genealogy studies and family trees. These stories are to entertain.

CHAPTER I

THE BAKER FAMILY

Kathryn, here are some stories you may pass on down to Liam, his cousins Ashley, Amanda, William and any others born in the new Millennium. This book may contain a lot more stories than you really wanted to read, but you can fast forward.

My Grandmother Baker (my Dad's Mother) told me stories when I was a little girl. She was so patient and gentle, but quite knowledgeable and interesting. I remember her holding me on her lap in the yard late one hot summer night to watch the shooting stars. She told me about Halley's Comet in 1910, and how scared people were when that happened.

Halley's Comet was named after Edmund Halley, who predicted its return after observing it in 1682. 1910 was the last appearance. So far???

She also told me a lot about my grandfather who died a month before I was born. Levi Baker was a prominent man in our town; president of a bank and did a lot of good deeds anonymously. For years, he wrote a gossip column in the local paper under a female name. No one ever discovered or suspected it was him.

He was also very interested in trains. If there had been model trains he would have had a room full. One night when she was waiting for him to come home she had a vision of him standing on the tracks with a train bearing down on him. It was so vivid it frightened her. She looked at the clock it was a few minutes after ten. When he showed up at about 11 o'clock she was relieved. She asked him where he had been at ten. He looked a little puzzled and said, "Well, I was standing on the railroad tracks at a crossing near town to see if the conductor of the train would signal if he saw me. He gave the proper signal and I stepped off the tracks". I heard this story many times during my early life.

He was quoted as saying he would hate to live in a community without churches, but did not feel the need himself. He was known as a very honest, charitable man who never attended, but gave money to the Congregational church because he liked and admired the minister. He claimed to be Unitarian, as was Thomas Jefferson. My grandfather Gass who owned the big General store told of him coming in and naming a family that was having a hard time,saying, "When they come in, give them anything they need and send the bill to me, but don't tell them who arranged to pay for it."

He also told of my brothers, Thad and Don when they were little, trying to get his attention. He ignored them, and acted like they weren't there. Finally, one said to the other, "You hit him and I'll pinch him and see if he notices."

He was also noted for never observing birthdays, Christmas, or any holiday, but was always giving presents to everyone.

He provided one big puzzle in my mind when I was little. I had a bank account with over $100 in it, an awesome amount in the 20s. We had little oval shaped, metal coin banks that we were taught to save our money in. It had a key hole and there was no way you could get the money out once you put it in the slot. ***(my brothers and I discussed this aspect)*** When it was full Dad would hold me up and the bank teller would open it with a key, count the money, deposit it to my account and write down the total in my little bank book. I was told that my grandfather Baker had left me and my brothers each $100. I also knew he had died a month before I was born so how did he know to leave it for me. Did he send me down from heaven with the $100? When the bank closed during the depression, the fact that I could no longer get my $135.75, changed my philosophy about saving money. At 16 when we were living in California, I received a notice from the bank in Iowa that $95 was the settlement from the bank. Everyone kept telling me how lucky I was to get that much back. I wanted to know where the other $40.75 was.

MY GREAT GRANDMOTHER

ELIZA SCOTT MARKS, was born December 22, 1823 in Seneca, New York and died on February 12, 1912. She graduated from Oberlin College, one of the first to admit women, and taught for one year. She and Willard T. Farnham, were married on May 17, 1850. In 1870 after an explosion at his black powder manufacturing company in Cleveland, Ohio, he sold out and bought 1200 acres of land in Iowa. Eliza's full autobiography is included in the book "Other Centuries; Other Stories".

This is a letter she had published in some periodical of the time in the late1800s. Her use of the English language is awesome. She was very active in the Women's Suffrage movement that eventually led to women being allowed to vote.

A GRANDMOTHER'S LETTER TO HER GRANDDAUGHTER

By Eliza M. Farnham

My Dear Granddaughter: You would like my views on the progressive development of the times. I will be happy to give them. History reveals a sad story of the religions of the past and the sad fate of millions of earth's brave and noble sons.

From the first, the crimson thread of fear is seen through all their teachings. Loving kindness was an unknown power, in dealing with the priceless mind of man. Exponents of religious thoughts were bitter enemies to intellectual advancement.

They destroyed the Alexandria library of 700,000 volumes, the contributions of many nations, an irreparable loss to the world.

In the pages of history I see one star shining brightly from the black night of a cruel and superstitious age. This star was Hypatia, the daughter of Theron, born in Alexandria, the latter part of the fourth century.

She was beautiful in person and mind, pure in heart and life, educated beyond her years. She assisted her father in his astronomical studies, succeeded him in his chair of science and delivered lectures, and was the pride of Alexandria. But that city was powerless to save her. She had been investigating the wonders of nature and the evil eye of the Bishop of Alexandria was upon her and he denounced her a heretic.

On her way home from her lecture room she was dragged from her chariot, stripped and torn to pieces with tiles and her limbs burned to ashes; thus a beautiful life went out to satisfy the hatred of the Bishop for a teacher's sacred mission. In future years many bright intellects met the same fate. In the sixteenth century, the twelve hundred years of the inquisition was nearing the end of its blood work. But persecutions went on.

In that century, when Gallileo pointed his telescope to the stars, and dared to talk of other worlds than ours, he was imprisoned, compelled to recant, and his instruments destroyed.

But they could not destroy the inventive genius of man and the star of hope grew brighter as the years went by. Our own times will tell you of the grand observatories that grace our civilization and of the master minds that work there, and their wonderful disclosures.

The crowing glory of the nineteenth century is the many and wonderful inventions wrought by the mind of man to bless our own and future generations. The civilized world is now interested in scientific studies; language cannot express the inspiring thoughts upon the subject.

But there is an appalling darkness upon the other side of this bright picture. That you will understand me, I will quote from two sermons that you may know the nature of the spiritual food given to starving minds in those days. This one I heard when about fifteen years of age. (1839) I can never forget it. The preacher said:

"Supposing a bird should take a grain of sand from the sea shore and fly away and be gone a thousand years and come back and take another grain of sand and be gone the same length of time, and so on until every grain of sand disappears. Then, your torture would have only just begun."

The immortal mind of man is the master work of Omnipotence, too sacred for such teachings. Happily there are dissenting voices. When the voice of the great commentator, Albert Barnes, was heard, he was dismissed from his pulpit—a grand advance—from the stake to a simple dismissal.

In sorrow and despair he said: "The difficulties of reconciling Scripture teachings to reason is probably felt by everyone who reflects upon the subject, and they are unexplained, unmitigated and unremoved." I for one feel them more sensibly and powerfully the more I look at them and the longer I live. I do not understand them and make no advance in understanding them. I do not know that I have a ray of light upon the subject, that I had met when the subject first flashed across my soul. I have read what wise and good men have written. I have looked at their theories and explanations. I have endeavored to weigh their arguments for my whole soul rants for light and relief on this question and in the anguish of my soul I confess I get no light whatever. I see not one ray of light to disclose to me why sin came into the world, why earth is strewn with the dying and the dead, and why man must suffer to all eternity. I never have seen one particle of light upon the subject that gives a moments ease to my tortured mind. When I see a world of sinners and sufferers, a world filled with hosts to suffer forever and ever, when I see my parents, my family and my fellow citizens involved in sin and danger, and see that the great masses are wholly unconcerned and feel that God alone can save them and yet He does not, I am struck dumb. It is all dark, dark, and I cannot disguise it.

Had that brave and noble teacher lived fifty years later he would now see in the dark clouds the silver lining of the bright day that is coming. The power that superstition has had over the minds of man is swiftly passing away. Science has scattered to the winds countless finalities from which there can be no appeal. We claim a right to question when reason, the bright gem of the soul, is lighting the way and the answer to one question is solved; that our star of hope will not go down in endless night. We are not left helpless. Infinite wisdom has implanted in our being, aspirations that all the powers of darkness cannot repress.

In this conflict of right and wrong, in the need of good and bad to educate and discipline, we realize the principal of Evolution, the grandest ever penned by human thought. But this principal of development has its enemies. Was there ever a step taken onward and upward in human progress that has not?

The first printing press in its building had to be guarded night and day in great secrecy, to prevent its destruction.

And again, I am speechless when I think of its immensity. It encircles the world with its daily news of passing events, sending its gathered treasures to every home to educate and entertain. Science is continually making new discoveries, forever at work developing principles that existed from all eternity. From the stars above us to the earth beneath our feet it is searching for facts and finding them regardless of consequences, revealing buried treasures not of gold but of far greater value: the past history of this planet. It is reading to us of a highly developed and cultured people who lived and disappeared from this earth before the dawn of history. This represents untold ages. The records that survive them are read like an open book.

We are the favored children of an advancing age. Wonders inconceivable to the present will yet appear, to the future possibilities of man there is no limit.

The universe of mind is moving on with restless power and in its onward course it broadens, elevates and purifies, and its mission to redeem the human race will be fulfilled. It is said in olden times that the Gods feared the supremacy of man.

Had they seen our day their fears would have been realized, but the Gods have disappeared, never to return, and only one immutable and eternal power reigns supreme through countless worlds, and endless space.

The beautiful world in which we live was once a vast ocean of liquid fire. Countless years have passed away, revealing the mighty changes that are taking place. In our time we are reading an interesting, but never-ending story of developments founded upon immutable laws, giving light and life to a dark and silent world. Think of the present, in view of that faraway time, and let us thank destiny, that in the evolutions of ages we have ourselves just where we are; never forgetting those who have gone before and what they have done to brighten the pathway of coming years; for the priceless liberties and intellectual advantages we now have. In contemplating upon the past and the present the grandeur of world building and the many dear associations of this life, did you ever think of the poverty of human language and feel that there is one of the soul that points to immortality? The intelligence and forethought manifested in the beginning comes to us as a divine inheritance; and loving kindness, knowing human needs, has given to our spiritual life a silent monitor that is ever-leading us upward to higher planes of thought. Read a history of its grand advance in the last century, and realize that we are the children of the first Great Cause and the crowing glory.

Your loving grandmother

ELIZA M. FARNHAM

Her letter sounds like a teacher, doesn't it? My Father had one of the first automobiles in Shenandoah, and my Mother told of taking her for a ride. She was really overwhelmed by the experience. Was a little scared, and couldn't believe how fast they were going.

CHAPTER II

THE GASS FAMILY

This chapter will be about Charlotte, Helen Gass (my mother) and her family.

There is a lot about the Gass family, starting with Thomas Topping, founder of the family in America. He was a religious refugee from England. In 1636 he lived in Weatherfield, Connecticut. He was one of the first settlers of Southampton, Long Island, New York. In New York he was a member of the Governor's Council, Captain of the Southampton Town Troops, Deputy to the Hempstead Assembly, Deputy Commissioner of Indian Affairs in the Province and Justice of the Peace. He died in 1688.

Sound like he was on more committees than your Grandpa

The Family Crest of the Topping Family is
"Toujours un Harmonie"
(Always in Harmony)

The name "Sanford" comes from this line. My great grandfather, George Sanford Gass, was born March 12, 1838 and died in 1932 at Mt. Pleasant, Iowa. George Sanford's mother Permelia was born June 10, 1811; died May 20, 1848. She married Elias Gass in Pennsylvania.

George Sanford Gass is doing extensive genealogy studies on this family. He is my cousin, and has been very much a part of our lives since he was five. Our common interest in photography has kept us in touch for more years than I care to count.

George Sanford Gass married Charlotte Morton in Greene Co. Pennsylvania. Their daughters were: Annie Morton who died at 15, Olive, who taught school in Colorado, Rachel Charlotte who lived all her life in Mt. Pleasant, Iowa taking care of him after their mother died. Rachel and Olive never married. Their son Harlan married Ruth Castle and resided in Shenandoah, Iowa. They had three sons, Paul Sanford, Richard Dale and Kenneth Earl. Kenneth died at an early age. Their son John Thomas (my grandfather) who owned the General Store in Shenandoah, Iowa, married Avesia O'Connor, when he was manager of the mining company store in Mendota, Missouri.

They had five children: Helen who married Eugene Baker, Shenandoah, Iowa—they had four children Thaddeus Ronald, Donald Farnham, Ernestine Avesia and Willard Thomas. ***This was my family.***

George Frederick who married Margaret Elizabeth Hunt. They had four children, Mary Margaretta, Robert Connor, Nathalie Ann, and George Sanford.

Harlan, who married Bea White. They had three children, Phyllis, Robert and Morton.

Marie, who married Raymond Sawyer. They had two sons, Thomas and John.

John Thomas, Jr., who married Edna Smith of Shenandoah and moved to Chicago. They had no children.

In the Topping genealogy I ran across a story that reflects Civil War times.

James Sanford, born April 5, 1804 in Green County, Pa, died 1889 in Pike Co., Ohio. He was known to everyone as "Uncle Jimmy" and was noted in his community for his strict honesty and fair dealing. Having furnished three sons for the Civil War, who were fighting for the Northern cause, and being a man who spoke his mind without mincing words, he was constantly in arguments during the war with some of his neighbors who were sympathetic to the Southern cause. To one who expressed the intention of returning to his old home in West Virginia and joining the Southern Army, "Uncle Jimmy" remarked that if he started, he would "get" him before he crossed the Ohio river. The neighbor decided to stay on his own side of the river.

My cousin, Bob Gass, took a trip to Ireland to search for information about the O'Connor and Shehan families. I remember "Ma" O'Connor. She never allowed anyone to call her "Grandma". I know she left Ireland and crossed the Ocean at age 13. She married O'Connor and lived in Mendota, Missouri. He was a cobbler. Avesia (my grandmother) was their first child. I have no information on the other four. The O'Connors split up after the children were gone. He moved and set up his cobbler shop in Lincoln, Nebraska. She traveled all over the country selling cosmetics she made, door to door. She lived until I was in my early teens, and I remember her well. She could dance a jig, and I can still hear her and Grandma giggle at the stories she told. We would always stop at Grandma Gass' when we went to town, and a couple of times I remember Grandma saying: "Ma should be here soon. Her trunks arrived today". ***Kinda reminds me of the internet joke: "Grandma walks ten miles a day, and has for the past five years. We don't know where she is now."***

It is believed Patrick Gass, who was on the Lewis and Clark Expedition, was an ancestor. Information about him will be in the book "Other Centuries; Other Stories".

AN OLD FASHIONED LOVE STORY

On August 1, 1892, Helen (Charlotte Helen) was born to John and Avesia Gass in Mendota, Missouri. He was the manager of the mining town's company store. They would have four more children, Marie, Harlan, George and John. Because there were no schools in Mendota, when Helen was eight she was sent to live with her grandfather, George Sanford Gass, in Mount Pleasant, Iowa, close to the Missouri border. He was a very stern, religious man who fought in the civil war to free the slaves. Her aunt Rachel, who took care of her father, acted as her surrogate mother. Her aunt Olive taught school in Denver and was also there part of the year.

They also sent her brother George with her the first year. She told how they arrived on the train in Mt. Pleasant, but nobody was there to meet them. Communications were not too good at the turn of the century. Someone finally saw their plight and told them how to get to the farm. It was several miles and they carried their suitcases and finally arrived. In later years, George told us of being so homesick that he would climb up on the roof of the barn and cry his heart out—after days of this he finally adjusted and said he had never been homesick ever again in his lifetime. When he was grown and married, they moved to Corning, California where he started an olive ranch that is still in his family. This family would become very important to us in the 40s when we were traveling back and forth from California to Washington.

The Gass family moved from Mendota to Shenandoah, Iowa and he opened up a large general store that sold everything needed for the home—food, clothing, patterns, yardage, jewelry, pots and pans and even toilet paper. Helen, remained at her grandfather's except for summer vacations at their home in Shenandoah.

In her late teens, she went with her sister, Marie to the local skating rink during one of her vacations. She met Eugene Baker, the son of the president of the bank, and it was "Love at first sight".

They returned to college that fall—he to Ames Agriculture College; she to Iowa Weslyan in Mount Pleasant to get her degree in Music. When they graduated in June 1914, they decided against a big wedding. With their parent's blessings, they eloped, a very popular, romantic fad at that time.

They lived at Eldorado, the old Farnham homestead mansion until 1922 when they had a new home built on the old Baker homestead. A small stream and a creek criss-crossed the 160 acre farm. In the center of the farm Eugene damned up the creek and made his "Walden" pond with a mulberry grove close by.

The pond was always a puzzle to me until after his death when my mother gave me some family books. One was Waldon Pond by Thoreau. I still treasure that book because it has notes written in the borders. It

gave me an insight to his thoughts as a young college student. It now gives me a feeling of understanding him as a person, not just as a parent.

Times were good for farmers in the 20s. Eugene was one of the first environmental farmers, and had one of the first steam tractors. He grew fields of soybeans before they were considered food in this country, allowed the pigs to eat the plants and fertilize the field, then plowed it all under to replenish nutrients in the soil. During the draught of 1933, he saved turtles by putting them in the horse watering tank. I often wonder what the horses thought of the snapping turtles in their drinking water. I know we missed our "swimming pool" during that searing hot summer.

In 1928 a brand new Chevrolet replaced the old Model T Ford, but soon the storms of the depression were brewing and farmers would be the first to feel the financial impact. They were able to hold onto their farm longer than many, but finally lost it and moved to California in 1936.

Their lives, like most, were filled with happiness, heartaches and tragedies. They lost their youngest son, Willard, on Leyte during World War II and worked in the defense industry until the war was over. They lost their oldest son, Thaddeus, at the age of 43 from a heart attack. But, they watched eight grandchildren grow to maturity, and celebrated their 60th anniversary together in Glendale, California before he departed at the age of 84.

In her late years, Helen's biggest complaint (with a chuckle) was that her son, Don, and daughter, Ernestine, were senior citizens. She lived to see some of her great, great grandchildren before joining Eugene at the age of 96.

Eugene and Helen Baker left a legacy to all whose lives they touched because, they cared.

CHAPTER III

STORIES OF THE 20's

We lived at Eldorado until I was two. This house was in our family until the 1960s. I don't have any memories of that house, except reoccurring dreams of a large, old house. There were many rooms with some scary, forbidden rooms you were not supposed to go into. ***(I'm sure the 3 story cupola was one of them)*** While visiting Mom when she was in her 90s, I told her about the dream and a small room with a round window. She said the room sounded like the nursery they made for me out of a big closet. Until 1936 when we moved to Hollywood, I remember picnics along the stream, and picking black walnuts in the orchard. The house was always occupied by tenants, so never went into the house. I do not know when, but part of it was moved across the road on another part of the farm to house tenants.

The old Baker homestead a mile and a half closer to Shenandoah became available to Dad when his father died. Dad had the old house torn down and a new, very modern home built on this property. We moved there when I was two years old. Two years later, my youngest brother Willard was born in that house. We lived on that farm until I was fifteen.

THE NEW HOME ON THE BAKER HOMESTEAD

My Baker great grandparents who homesteaded the 160 acres, deeded one corner acre for the schoolhouse. It was fairly close to our new home, with an orchard and a few acres in between.

Before I was old enough for school, I would go to the schoolyard fence and watch the older kids playing.

The commercial crops were corn and wheat. There were the usual animals found on farms, raised for food and for sale. We had a big barn, with a hay mow in the middle and stalls for horses on one side and cows on the other. The hen house with many chickens provided eggs and baby chicks, and there were always pigs to provide sausage, bacon, hams and pork chops.

We had electricity from a DELCO Plant (gasoline fed generator). As far as I know, we were the only family outside of town who had electricity. Dad and his father were great admirers of Thomas Jefferson, and many features of Montecello would be built into that home. The basement was built into a hill with part of it above ground for driveway access to the one car garage. Mom would drive to town in the Model T Ford to shop. When we got home she would drive the car into the garage, and we would all pile out and help load the groceries and stuff into the dumb waiter. It was big enough to carry all the groceries plus a couple of kids if we could talk Mom into letting us, or if she forgot and locked the door at the top of the stairs. The dumb waiter was then pulled up to the kitchen area by ropes on a pulley. The only dumb waiter I saw at Monticello was built the same, but was just big enough to hold two wine bottles. I wondered if they had a bigger one somewhere else, or if ours was just a practical one Dad designed. It was like him to do that. In Monticello the servants worked in the underground section, prepared and sent food up to the dining room and did all the laundry and chores out of sight from the main living quarters.

The middle part of our basement area had small daylight windows and was where the laundry was done, the milk separated and the coal stored to feed the furnace. This furnace supplied steam heat to radiators, and hot water to the kitchen and bathroom. Very, very modern for those times. We also had an electric motor, fueled by gasoline, to pump the water from our well into the house. When appliances became available, we would have a wringer washing machine and an electric refrigerator, but that would not be until electric power lines came out from town.

The back of the basement which was underground, below the front part of the house, was cold storage. It was dark and cool with no windows. We stored home canned food, potatoes, apples and a large crock of sauerkraut in this area. There was one acre for growing food such as cabbage, potatoes, carrots, lettuce, radishes, green onions, cucumbers and squash, plus Concord grape vines at one end. All over the 160 acres were many mulberry trees, and close to the house we had apple and peach trees. In season, we also picked gooseberries, crab apples, wild strawberries and tiny, tart wild grapes.

As the picture shows, it looked like a one story house from the front and three stories at the back. The attic had hard-wood floors like the main floor, with dormer windows for more rooms if needed. It was a memorable attic and made a wonderful play area during winter months. The center part (48 feet long) made a great roller skating rink. It must have been pretty noisy downstaris, because we weren't allowed to skate if visitors came. I remember some spooky Halloween parties, and later dances. Behind the rafters there were some interesting things to explore.

Most medical problems were taken care of at home, especially when you lived in the country. Doctors were only called for real serious problems. Dad's uncle, Dr. Baker, was a Homeopathic doctor, and supplied Dad with the many remedies of that profession. The first time I ever saw a medical doctor was when at six, I fell off a galloping horse and broke my arm. I was taken to a doctor in town. It was a compound fracture at the wrist, and looked terrible. I thought it would have to be cut off, and was surprised when we walked out of the doctor's office and my fingers were still there, hanging out the edge of two boards with my arm in a sling.

When you had a cold, measles, chicken pox or any illness, you were immediately put to bed, fed hot soups and little white homeopathic pills, and sometimes quinine. No going to school with a cold or any illness. Before antibiotics no chances were taken on the possibility of pneumonia. Quinine and laxatives are the only medicines I remember. Quinine was used as a tonic after a bad cold or flu. We did have iodine, bag balm, carbolated vasoline and Mecca compound for cuts and skin infections. We still keep a supply of the

Mecca Compound, but have only found it in Canada. Band-aids had not been invented yet. Old sheets were cut up and used as bandages and sometimes fastened with a safety pin, or tied on with string. I remember when Kleenex first came on the market, and Grandma Gass showing us these funny paper handkerchiefs.

HAIRCUT—CIRCA 1926

"Willie, come on and get your face washed. Katie's comin' to see us."

Willie stamps his foot. "No! Face awright! Katie 'uves me anyway!"

"Well, if you wash your face maybe Mom'll let you watch her cut Katie's hair. I heard them talkin' on the phone."

Mom was a modern woman. She drove the new Model T Ford; she played auction bridge; she had bobbed her hair, and even used Tangee lipstick! (although I wasn't supposed to tell anyone) Katie, Mom's best friend, was one of our favorites. She and Walter didn't have any kids of their own, and when she picked you up and hugged you, she smelled like Naptha soap and homemade bread. Her starter rolls with fresh butter and jam were always a treat we looked forward to when Willie and I rode to town with Mom and Katie.

Katie arrived with some cookies, still warm from the oven. Willie and I settled down on the kitchen floor (out of the way, of course) so we could eat our cookies and watch this very important event. I couldn't imagine Katie with bobbed hair! She was a large, chubby woman with straight, black hair done up in a big bun at the back of her neck. Mom said she talked a little different than us because she came from Kentucky.

Mom's hair was naturally curly and black which made her blue eyes really stand out. They said she got her "coloring" from her grandmother who came over from Ireland on a ship when she was thirteen. Katie had dark eyes, almost black, and what would she look like with straight, black hair that had been bobbed? Besides, I had heard all kinds of stories about the women around town who had bobbed their hair. Mr. Marshall, the only man in town with a beard, said until his wife's hair grew back as long as before he would let his beard grow. His beard was already long and bushy, like the pictures you see in history books.

On the phone this morning, I had heard Mom trying to talk Katie out of having her hair cut, but Katie was determined! I would have to remember to ask Mom what "divorce" meant. I overheard Mom telling Dad one day that Walter had threatened to divorce Katie if she ever cut her hair.

Now the hair-cutting stool was set up in the kitchen. The linoleum on the floor with the pretty pattern made cleaning up the hair real easy. When it was warmer, Mom cut hair on the back porch, and when it was real hot in the summer it was done in the basement. She did all the haircutting for our family, Grandpa Gass and a few friends. Mom used to cut our hair with scissors and clippers you had to squeeze. Now she had the new electric clippers that Dad brought home.

Mom was still trying to talk Katie out of it when I heard the buzz of the new electric clippers. Well, it was too late now—one side of Katie's head was bobbed! It looked so different! When the haircut was finished, Mom gave Katie a hand mirror. And after a first surprised look, Katie grinned and said "Oh, Helen, if that don't beat all! It's just the way I wanted it!

After some tea and more cookies, we drove her home in the Model T. I was hoping Walter would be there and I would get to see all the excitement and maybe find out what "divorce" meant, but he was in the barn milking the cows, so we'd have to wait until tomorrow to hear what he said about her bobbed hair.

The next morning the phone rang three longs and a short (our number). Mom rushed to the phone. "Really? Ten o'clock? I can't believe it! Well, I guess he can't really say much then, huh? Well, I'm glad. I think it looks nice and I know you are really going to like having it short. It's so easy to take care of. I'll pick you up tomorrow and we'll go to town. How about looking at some patterns at my Dad's store?"

Willie was tugging at my dress, knowing something important was happening. I could hardly wait 'till Mom hung up. "What did Walter say, Mom? What did he say?"

"Well, that really takes the cake! He didn't even notice it all evening. Finally at ten o'clock Katie couldn't stand it any longer and told him to look at her hair. And, you know what? He really likes it!"

I forgot to ask Mom what "divorce" means.

COUNTRY SCHOOL DAYS

Last Saturday, I slept overnight at my best friend's house, and Sunday we went to a big Swedish family reunion. There must have been a hundred people there and lots of food all day long. Doris' mother had made us new dresses just alike. We both have blue eyes and our blond hair cut in what Mom calls a "Dutch Bob" with bangs in front and cut straight just below the ears. Many of the people at the picnic thought we were twins. We are the same height and weight which makes it great for playing on the Teeter Totter. She is a little older than I am and is in the fourth grade.

Well, today at school we were having a lot of fun on the teeter totter until Richard pushed me off when she was up in the air. I got up and started punching him real hard! All the kids were standing around us. We were down on the ground and really pounding on each other. I don't know which of us was winning. Suddenly, I was on my feet with the teacher yanking on my dress. She had broken up the fight; recess was over.

When we got back into our seats, the teacher announced to the whole school that I was to stay after school for an hour. Richard didn't get any punishment and the teacher never asked us what the fight was all about.

At five o'clock I was told I could go home. When I came out of the school house, I saw Richard coming up Bingham Road just across the highway from the school. I went over to talk to him. He was still mad, but not at me. He was mad at the teacher for punishing me. Then, he pulled out a gun from his pocket and said he was going to shoot her with his Dad's 38. I was scared and told him he shouldn't, and that the teacher only thought girls shouldn't fight like boys do. After talking some more, he finally decided to put the gun back in his pocket and go home.

When I got home, I hurried and gathered the eggs from the henhouse and started helping Mom get dinner ready. She didn't say anything about my being late. I guess my brothers Thad and Don had already told her and Dad about my fight. I decided to keep it a secret about Richard and his Dad's gun.

ENTERTAINMENT

Living on a farm, there were no vacations, but all through the year we celebrated family birthdays, New Year's Eve, April Fool's Day, Memorial Day, July Fourth, Halloween, Thanksgiving and Christmas. At school we celebrated Lincoln and Washington's birthdays on their birthdays (not President's Day) and on May Day (the first day of May) we made little baskets, filled them with candy and flowers and left them at our favorite friend's house. We would knock on the door or ring their doorbell and run, watching them find it while we hid behind a bush. June, July and August were non-school months, and the Fourth of July was the big summer holiday. Firecrackers, rockets, sparklers and the carbide cannon punctuated great feasts of hot dogs, hamburgers, potato salad and of course watermelon. In September, school started On Labor Day (it was not a holiday). Holidays were not changed to make three-day weekends like they are now.

Other events were Air Shows, a Circus with a big parade, County and State Fairs, local gatherings for Farm Bureau events, football, baseball and basketball. For a brief period, I remember a fad called "Marathon Dances" that swept the country. The last couple standing won a large sum of money. Sometimes they danced for days, taking turns sleeping while they continued dancing.

In our family, teasing was a form of getting attention, or showing someone you liked them but were too bashful to say so. Humor was a very important facet of life and you soon learned to "see behind" the words and actions. The first real clown I saw though, left me puzzled and confused.

THE BALL GAME

I was about four years old when my Father announced we were going to the fairgrounds to see a baseball game. Not having been to school where they played baseball, it didn't mean much to me, but a trip to the fairgrounds was always exciting.

There was the smell of dust, people, popcorn and peanuts in the air. People were walking around with cones of bright colored fluff. Now I know it was cotton candy, and yes they did have it back in the 20's. I also know why we weren't treated to that delight—sticky, sticky, sticky! I also saw balloons with a string to hold them from flying up into the air, and a few that had escaped into the sky; not like the ones we blew up ourselves. There were men in white coats selling popcorn and peanuts. Dad did buy some of those for us.

I was busy observing the people around me and enjoying the treats. That was about all I could see! All of a sudden, it seemed the audience went crazy and someone yelled "Home Run!".

Sitting there like a good little girl, I was hit on the head by something very hard, and all of a sudden I was the center of attention instead of the ball game. In the confusion, I saw a man dressed up in a funny striped suit with a big smile on his face. I remember feeling insulted that a grown-up, even if he was dressed funny, would make fun of me and laugh because I was hurt. When he came close I saw that his face was just painted with a big smile. Underneath all the paint, his mouth and especially his eyes were not smiling. He was really afraid that I had been badly hurt.

Well, I survived the bump with only a big knot on my forehead and the ball game went on. This was not the first or the last bump I would get in life, but I did learn something that day. Don't judge people by how they look, or dress. We've all heard the statement "The eyes are the windows of the soul." At four it would not have meant much to me; now I know what it means and realize what a valuable lesson I learned as a very little girl.

SHOPPING (NO MALLS)

The Sears catalog was part of life on the farm in Iowa. Farm implements, harness for the horses, milk buckets and cans, everything needed for the kitchen and especially for canning. They sold furniture, toys, clothes, shoes and even complete materials and plans to build elaborate houses.

I would be thirteen years old before I went to a big city and saw department stores, large restaurants, and a Woolworth 5 & 10 cent store where everything really was 5 & 10 cents. In Shenandoah, there were no buildings over five stories.

On the farm, outside a small town of less than 5,000 people, almost everything came from the catalog. Montgomery Wards (we called it Monkey Wards) also was a large mail order company with competitive catalogs. Shenandoah had a drug store with a soda fountain, a bank, general store that had clothing, yardage, food and other needed items. The J.C. Penney store had clothing, shoes and some toys. The clerks sent the money up to their office in little containers on a rail. Your change and receipt came back down the rail. The town also had a post office, hospital, elementary school and a high school. Country schools went through eighth grade and high school was four years. In town, they did have kindergarten and an elementary school. This was before junior high or what they now call middle schools.

My Father taught me not to be disappointed if something did not turn out just like I planned. How? Would you believe with the help of Sears Roebuck catalogs. My "pay" for all the chores I did on the farm was one quarter a week, and Grandpa Gass would give us quarters when we went to his store. I would see something in the catalog and save and save until I had enough quarters to buy the "good" item. Most items had three pictures of each marked "Good", "Better", or "Best" with comparable prices. Dad would take my frugally saved coins and send the order in for me. He never explained or said anything about shipping charges. Then when the package arrived, he "read" a letter to me saying they didn't have the item I ordered, but sent something else. This would upset me after all the hours I had spent choosing and saving, but when the package was opened, to my delight, it was always the "best" or at least the "better".

I don't know how many times I heard the warning "Always hope for the best, but expect the worst". Instead, I developed my own philosophy of life "Always expect the good, and not be disappointed if it turned out to be something different because it would probably be better if not the best. The National Geographic was my window to the world, but Sears Roebuck catalog was my shopping mall.

Many of the big disappointments of life have turned out in the long run to be better than I had ever hoped. Sometimes it takes years to realize why. But look back on your life and count the many times that disappointments really opened up new opportunities that could

not have happened if life had given you what you thought you wanted. I now call them detours. I think we have had more detours than most, or maybe we have just been more venturesome.

FOURTH OF JULY AND THE CANNON

This was a big event for all of the families. I am sure the cousins who lived in Shenandoah will all remember the fireworks display put on every year. Sometimes there would be as high as 20 at our dining room table. Everyone brought something and we had all kinds of food. Fireworks and firecrackers weren't allowed in town so everyone gathered at the farm. Raymond Sawyer, our uncle, always brought spectacular rockets, and there were always sparklers, cap guns and varying sizes of firecrackers. But, best of all, was the cannon.

My Dad told of buying the carbide cannon the first year they had them for sale. He was assured it was completely safe, so he took it home. They lived in the old Farnham mansion at that time. He set it up on the kitchen table to show Mom. Following the directions exactly, he set it off. After the explosion and the smoke had cleared, they both looked around to see if the house was still there. It was safe, the house was still standing, but from then on it was an outdoor event. They also told of Ma O'connor, (our great grandmother) coming out and taking it down the road a piece to where there was a culvert. She and my two brothers would hide in the culvert and wait until they heard a car coming and then set the cannon off. On a dirt road, the drivers were sure a tire had blown. She would giggle and they would watch the driver get out and check all the tires.

I remember my brothers and I using it the same way years later when we lived in the new house on the highway, except we just did it in a hidden area of the porch. Later, Don and Thad rigged it up with the model train transformer, so we could set it off without using matches. Yes, they did have model trains in those days. The carbide cannons are still advertised in catalogs and look exactly the same.

HALLOWEEN

In the early years of this Century, Halloween was more TRICK than TREAT. The teenagers got rid of their frustrations by ever-increasing sophisticated tricks, such as putting wagons on top of barn roofs, and later cars on top of town buildings.

One of the most popular and simpler tricks was to push over outhouses. Usually it was the town's young men who hiked out into the countryside.

In preparation for Halloween, my grandfather, Levi, prepared for this event, and set the outhouse back of the pit. It was dark and he had picked a spot behind a tree near the outhouse to watch the fun. Soon he heard a commotion as a group of five or six young men rushed toward the outhouse with their hands and arms poised to do the trick.

The one in the lead fell in; the others were able to stop just before tumbling in after him. They immediately turned and ran for town. Their unfortunate companion wasted no time crawling out and running after them shouting for them to wait for him.

I am sure the "Treat" part of Halloween was dreamed up by the elders to discourage the destructive "Tricks". Over the years, most of the Trick or Treaters really didn't know what the "Trick" part meant and it became a very special fun night for the little ones. Now, the children go in groups or are accompanied by parents to protect them! Or, communities, and individuals are providing organized and supervised parties, like we had in our attic.

We didn't play trick or treat in our generation—at least not in the country. I do remember some parties in the attic where Grandma Gass, dressed in a witches costume, read fortunes from cards.

She would laugh with a true witches "cackle" while reading our fortunes.

CHRISTMAS

Christmas was a time of giving. I learned the joy of giving, and realized early in life that it really is far better to give than to receive. Gifts were simple and few. We went out in the woods and found a Christmas tree. Dad and the older boys cut it down and carried it into the house.

We decorated the tree with popcorn and cranberry strings, foil icicles and decorative ornaments. In the late 20's there would be electric Christmas lights. We never used candle ornaments because of the fire hazard. The families in Shenandoah, Grandpa and Grandma Gass and Phyllis (my cousin who lived with them), Raymond and Marie Sawyer and their two boys Tom and John would be out for a Christmas get together and exchanging of gifts. Bob and Mort (Phyllis' brothers) and their parents, Harlan and Bea Gass would sometimes be in Shenandoah for the holidays. They lived in Omaha, Nebraska a big city 60 miles from Shenandoah.

Packages would arrive from all over the country. Chicago, New Orleans, Colorado and California, mostly from my Father's side of the family. Later my Mother told me she used to unwrap all the packages sent to the four of us, record what they contained and what each of us received and who it was from. Then she would re-wrap them all and put them under the tree. After Christmas she would write thank you notes. When we were old enough to write she would make sure we wrote the thank you notes. We helped wrap and make good things to give to neighbors, relatives and friends at Christmas and at other times too. You never went to anyone's house without a gift—maybe a jar of jam, home-baked bread or cookies. We were allowed to pick one present from the Sears catalog in a certain price range. By the time we chose, we had "owned" a lot of others.

THE NATIONAL GEOGRAPHIC

In the twilight years, my mind wanders back to the simple life on the farm and the feeling as a child of being a part of a vast universe. I poured over those old black and white Geographics, trying to visualize the size of the world I lived in. The world that seemed so big and wondrous on the farm is still big and wondrous, even if I have learned it is just a small speck in the universe.

In the 20s, our country mailbox brought us letters from relatives, the magazines and packages and of course that important Sears Roebuck catalog! We were taught very early in life that other people's mailboxes were strictly to be left alone and that if anything was "all powerful" it was Washington D.C. and our Federal Government.

The mail plane that flew over the farm every day was delivering especially important mail. In the 20s, the country mailbox was the link to our government in Washington, D.C. and everyone had a healthy regard and respect for our Federal Government.

By the mid 20s, clothing styles began to change drastically. It was the age of women's liberation. They were starting to drive cars, bob their hair (cut it really short), join women's clubs and play bridge. Boys wore Levi's that looked just like they do now. Girls wore very simple dresses, skirts and blouses. Slacks were non-existent, but I wore my brother's levis whenever I could get away with it. Clothes faded and most were washable, but wash and wear would be far into the future, so everything had to be ironed. After all the technology developed to produce material that would not fade or wrinkle, it has become the fad now to buy clothing that looks faded and wrinkled. Aren't people strange?

SCHOOL DAYS IN THE 20'S

The Golden Rule "Do unto others as you would have them do unto you" was a simple, easy to understand code. It is written in many different languages. As with any rule, it was sometimes broken. Teachers were allowed to punish, and the hickory stick was a branch off of a tree. Some teachers abused this privilege. I saw one boy's hand badly cut when the teacher struck him repeatedly with the sharp metal edge of a ruler. They sometimes kept you after school for an hour if you misbehaved.

The country schools in 1925 were small, one-room buildings and served a community of several square miles. One teacher taught all grades from first through the eighth and usually there were never more than 25 students total, ages six to eighteen. Students walked to school. In some areas they rode horses. There were no buses, and cars were not used for trivial errands like transporting kids to school. In some areas, the teachers, who were very poorly paid, roomed and boarded at student's homes, traveling from home to home during the school year. This allowed them to become acquainted with the parents and evaluate social or learning problems of the students. I don't ever remember any boy or girl who could not read.

Hours were from eight in the morning until four in the afternoon with a lunch period and several recesses. We were taught only reading, writing and arithmetic in the first few grades. Upper grades studied history, civics (study of our government) grammar and spelling. Since all students were in the same room, you heard other classes reciting and watched them writing on the blackboards while being taught. You sort of learned by osmosis, just being in school for a full eight hours every day.

We saluted the flag and sang songs. My favorite was:

School Days, School Days,
Good ol' Golden Rule Days.
You were my queen in calico.
I was your bashful, barefoot beau.
You wrote on my slate "I love you Joe",
When we were a couple of kids.

During recess we played baseball (this was before softball), active games called ten-step, tag and had races around the outside of the school building. We also had teeter-totters and swings.

There was a hand water pump. We all drank from the same dipper that hung on the pump until a new teacher who had studied about germs, insisted we all bring our own cup from home. We thought this was pretty dumb, but our folks bought us funny little aluminum cups that folded up and could be put in our desks.

There were no rest rooms—only two privies at the back of the acre lot. One teacher made a new rule that we had to hold up our hand with one finger if we wanted to pee and two fingers if we wanted to do the big job. I thought this was very embarrassing, and the few times I had to go, I just got up and went out. She never reprimanded me for it. The schoolroom at first was heated by a big, wood-burning stove where on cold days you sat around that area to keep warm. Later a more modern wood-burning furnace was put in the basement.

I hated spelling bees. On written spelling tests I always got very high grades, but when we had to get up and spell outloud in front of all the kids, I would deliberately mis-spell the first word so I could sit down. I think the teacher thought I was cheating on the paper work because she kept a close watch on me. I wonder if she ever figured it out.

During the early part of the century, and up actually until World War II, most teachers were single. The country school was usually their first job and their ambition was to eventually get married or become a town teacher. Some would devote their lives to teaching. Even in 1936, it was unusual for a school to accept a married teacher in most of the country.

I suppose there are some areas where the small country schools still exist, but most have become Consolidated Schools with bus service to provide transportation and gymnasiums to provide the exercise.

THE OYSTER FEED

My folks were quite active in the Farm Bureau. One day, after a meeting, my father came home and announced that the next Saturday there would be a family dinner party in town. He said they were going to have Oyster Stew.

As usual, all the kids were seated at one table, and the adults at other tables. They set a bowl of milky stuff in front of us and there was a bowl of funny little round "baby" crackers. I watched the older kids and they put a few of the baby crackers in the soup. Then I saw these funny looking gray pieces in the soup. Marie, the oldest at our table was sitting next to me. She was already in High School. I stirred the stuff up a little and she leaned over and said. "Do you know what oysters are?" "No", I said, "What are they?" "They're mice turned wrong side out" she said with a grin. I quietly ate my crackers and soup, but didn't eat the oysters.

After moving to the west coast, I was introduced to many new foods I'd never even heard of before. It was interesting going to the Chinese restaurants and I loved that food. The Mexican hot stuff took a little getting used to. Oysters would wait until we moved to the Northwest and camped where we picked oysters and learned how to grill them. I still picture in my mind, my Father sitting at a picnic table at Twano State Park with a heap of oyster shells at his plate. He asked Ash to bring him some more. Ash said "Dad, that's pretty rich food, are you sure it won't make you sick?" Dad said, "Bring me some more; I'll tell you when I'm getting sick!"

THE COUSINS

I had nine cousins on my Mother's side of the family—Phyllis, Bob and Mort Gass, Tom and John Sawyer, and four who I wouldn't meet until we moved to California, Connor, Margaretta, Nathalee Ann and George (Sandy). When all the cousins came out to the farm we usually split up into two groups. Sometimes we played competitive games as teams; other times we just did different things on the farm. On Dad's side there was only one cousin our age—his sister Louise's daughter also named "Ernestine" but called "Nern". She lived with her parents, Louise and Ray Lawson, on a ranch in Colorado. They visited once when she was about eight. It was mulberry picking time and we decided to scare the grownups and paint our faces with mulberry juice, put a band on our hair with chicken feathers stuck in it. Well, it worked—the parents were shocked when we came in whooping it up with a toy drum and did an Indian dance for them. We found out later why they were shocked—it took days for the stain to come off and we were grounded from going to town until it did. A very sad thing happened a few years later. She died of a brain tumor.

Tom Sawyer tells of some of the mischief he and Willard got into—getting into the schoolhouse and playing the organ. He also said he and Willard found out chickens could swim—they put some in the horse tank and they swam. During the hot summer, we all used the horse tank as a small swimming pool, except for the summer of the draught when Dad put the snapping turtles in the tank to save them.

I remember one time when Tom and I were out playing and it was getting late. It was my job to gather the eggs each day, but we were so far from the house we decided to just put them in our coat pockets instead of getting the basket. On our way back, we wanted to go see the calves in the barnyard. We all liked to teach them to drink when they were little by putting our hand down in the milk and letting them suck on it. As we climbed over the fence, Tom fell into a fresh cow pie and the eggs in his pockets broke. Just then, we heard Mom call us to dinner. I don't remember any big fuss. Mom, a mother of four, seemed to face dilemmas like this very calmly.

Phyllis and I were climbing a big split oak tree one day. When we started to climb back down we saw the biggest bull snake ever, also coming down at the split. We were about to meet head on. We scrambled back up and hung on a long branch to drop to the ground. We told Dad about it and he hunted it down. He said it was so big—over six feet long—that it could hurt a kid or small animal. They were not poisonous, but could bite like a rat. They were considered valuable because they did kill and eat rats, mice and other varmints.

BE HAPPY

This was written many years ago, inspired by an experience told by Lorena Gass, my cousin Bob's wife. He was in the Air Force and they were stationed in Newfoundland. I made up this story about her experience for an assignment in a writing class.

In Newfoundland, I watched a group of children playing "Ring Around the Rosie". They could have been children from anywhere in the world. Typical of so many child groups, there was one forlorn little fellow on the outside. His eyes showed his inner desire to join the game, but for some reason he was an outcast. I wondered what he had done to warrant this isolation. Were the children just being cruel to him? My heart went out to him because I could remember so clearly the feeling of being an outsider when I stood outside the school yard fence , before I was old enough to go to school, and watched the older kids play. Should I stop the game and ask the children to let him in?

I was startled when a very plain lady, obviously his mother, sized up the situation with one swift glance, slapped his face and said, "Get in there and BE HAPPY!"

Before I could protest, the little boy jumped into the group, grabbed a hand on each side and was instantly happy, accepted by the others without a second glance.

How wise of this mother to realize that the isolation came, not from the cruelty of others, but just their indifference. Being accepted is an inner thing.

Are you standing on the outside of life? Then grab somebody's hand and BE HAPPY!

MY FIRST LESSON IN NUTRITION

Food was very important before radio and television. On a farm it was a major part of life. Feeding the animals was a chore given to children at a very early age. My parents were very knowledgeable and careful about the food we ate. "No dessert until you clean your plate"!

"Did you know there are children in China that are starving?"

At five years of age, I spent a lot of time in the orchard near our home while my older brothers were in school. I loved to watch the birds, pick violets and dandelions and just think about things like five year olds do. One day a little squirrel got curious about me and came quite close. I talked to him quietly and each day he came a little closer. I tried to pet him but he always dodged and scurried away, climbing up high in a tree, but still watching me. By this time, of course, I had named him "Skinny".

I asked my father one day what squirrels eat. He said they ate nuts and probably would eat corn. Being a corn farm, there was plenty of that. The field corn in the granary was hard and I took some kernels and put them in my apron pocket.

The next day "Skinny" came close enough I could reach out my hand and show him the corn. He finally got brave enough to take one kernel, but he ate part of it and threw the rest away. The day after that, I held the corn close to me and he hopped up on my knee and started eating away. I then noticed that he took each kernel, dug out a small soft part with his sharp eye tooth and threw the rest away.

That evening I told my Dad about "Skinny" hopping up on my knee and eating the corn out of my hand. Then, I asked him why he threw away most of the corn and only ate the part that was closest to the cob. He told me that was what they called "The germ" and when you planted the kernels, the germ was the part that grew the new corn stalks we had in the fields. I couldn't believe those tall stalks grew from that little, tiny part of the kernel.

Skinny and I continued our ritual, and when he grew fatter he went on to other pursuits.

This was not before white flour, but it was before our many processed foods. We cooked wheat just harvested for cereal. It took a long time and was kind of chewy but tasted better than the oatmeal Mom bought in town. Later we would have Shredded Wheat, Corn Flakes and white cream of wheat. My second lesson in nutrition was in a chemistry class in high school—but that's another story I'll tell later.

WRITING

In first grade I learned to write words. Every day we had penmanship lessons to help improve our handwriting. In the first few grades, we were only taught reading, writing and arithmetic. I soon learned to read well enough to enter every contest offered in the magazines that came in the mail. For writing something good about a product in twenty-five words or less, you could win a prize. When I received a package in the mail, I was so excited. Inside I found a beautiful fountain pen that you could fill with ink. I didn't know anyone in school who had one of the new pens you didn't have to dip in ink. Then I saw what was written on the pen "Exlax really works!" We all knew what Exlax was! I never showed it to anyone, but I was hooked on writing.

This is how I might have written about the tornado I survived when I was six years old.

THE TORNADO

I am six years old and through with first grade. Don and Thad are in third and fifth grades and Willie, the baby is only two years old.

Last night I heard Dad and Mom talking about a reunion (whatever that is). Thad is going to stay with Dad to help with the farm work and Mom will drive the rest of us to her grandfather's home in Mount Pleasant.

After school today, I told Don what I'd heard and asked if he knew where Mt. Pleasant was. He said, "No, but in geography class they taught me how to look it up." We went to our library next to the fireplace and he showed me a book that had what he called "Maps". He finally pointed to a spot on the map of Iowa and said, "There it is! It looks like it's clear on the other side of Iowa near the Mississippi River. Get me a ruler and I can figure out how many miles." He's so smart! I got the ruler and he put it on the map and said, "It looks like about 300 miles and a little bit more from Shenandoah. That's going to take a long time to get there."

Mom is a very smart woman. She drives our Model T Ford to town and Farm Bureau meetings and all over, but never 300 miles!!! I heard more about the reunion listening to Mom and aunt Marie talking on the phone. It was our Great Grandpa's 90th birthday and we would be there for a week. Grandma, Marie and our cousin Tom Sawyer would probably go on the train and meet us there. Tom is not the boy I've read about in school.

Mom has told me about living with her Grandpa and her two aunts, Rachel and Ollie. After packing our suitcases and saying good-bye to Dad and Thad, we climbed into the car. About an hour later, we passed through Clarinda, the county seat. That was the farthest east we'd ever been. Don had a pencil and paper and was putting some numbers down. He leaned over and showed me that if we went 30 miles per hour it would take us about ten hours. If Mom drove faster, which she often did, he figured we might get there in eight hours. We had left about 7 o'clock after a quick breakfast, and had food packed in baskets on the floor under our feet. When we stopped for gasoline, we all went to the bathroom and when we got hungry, Mom and Don spread out a blanket alongside the road and we ate out of the picnic basket. I slept some of the time and Willie slept most of the time like little kids do. The road was really straight and the farms didn't look any different than around Shenandoah.

When we got to Great Grandpa Gass' farm a mile or two outside of Mt. Pleasant, I saw a man who looked like the pictures in the history book that told about President Lincoln. Great Grandpa was tall, thin, stood very straight and had a beard. Mom said he was very proud that he had fought in the Civil War to free the slaves. First grade doesn't study history, but we listen all day to the older kids and the teacher when they study about it, so I knew a lot about the Civil War.

There were all kinds of good food, and the grownups were laughing and talking. We kids had fun playing on the farm. While we were playing outside one day the sky turned dark and there was a lot of rumbling thunder. The adults came rushing out and shooed us all into the house and down in the cellar. They tried to get Grandpa to join us but he just sat there in his rocking chair, with his Bible in his lap and said, "If it's my time to go the Good Lord will take me."

In the dark basement, huddled in the corner, it was scary listening to the rumble and noise of the storm. Suddenly the noise stopped and we all went upstairs. Mom and Aunt Rachel ran upstairs to close some windows, and came rushing back down. Mom said they looked right up into the funnel with all kinds of things blowing around inside, but it lifted up over the house. It was very quiet, and then came the pelting rain and hail. A few windows were broken, and trees were down, but nobody was hurt. Grandpa was still in his rocker just watching all the commotion.

In just a little bit the storm was gone and the sun came out. Mom went to the front door and shouted "Rachel, Rachel, come here! Wasn't there a house over in the next field???" Rachel rushed to the door and said "Oh, no! I wonder if John and Mary and the baby are all right? The next day we drove around to see the terrible damage done by that tornado. The three story house was just a pile of splinters. John, Mary and the baby were dropped into the basement. They were hurt, but the baby was killed.

When I went to bed that night, I couldn't forget all that had happened—my Great Grandfather in his rocker ready to be taken if it was his time to go. But, why would God let a little baby be killed? When I asked Mom the next morning, she said "Grandpa believes that God is all powerful. I believe He is all good. If He were all powerful, he wouldn't have let the baby be killed."

WORDS OF WISDOM FROM MY MOTHER

Look before you leap.

How would you like it if they did that to you! (her Golden Rule)

Oh, Tunket! I just spilled the milk!

Salmon in the ditch. Where did I put that pair of scissors?

On my first date—Act like a lady and you'll be treated like a lady.

Always wear clean underwear; you might be in an accident.

God is not all powerful, so if you get in trouble you have to get yourself out of trouble.

And, *YOU CAN JUST GO WAY BACK AND SIT DOWN!*

When you heard this, you knew you were in trouble! I heard her tell her crusty old doctor that back when they made house calls. I don't think he knew how much trouble he was in!

CHAPTER IV

STORIES OF THE 30's

Kathryn, when you were in elementary school, you came home one day when we were there, put your books on the dining room table and said "We studied about the big depression in history today. Your Grandpa looked surprised and said, "How would you like to hear about it from someone who was there?" You stared at each other. I think you could not understand Grandpa ever being anywhere but there, and he was pondering the fact that he was history. Just then, there was a scratch at the door. It was Casey, the cat who had trained Grandpa to be the door keeper. The conversation ended there and was never discussed again. Maybe this chapter will tell you more than your history books did about what it was like living during the great depression.

PRESIDENTIAL ELECTIONS

In 1932, the night before the presidential election, I witnessed the power of radio. The country was in deep trouble. The depression really hit the farmers.

My father, a "died-in-the-wool—vote-a-straight-ticket" Republican, was listening to a man talking on our new Atwater Kent radio. It was the first radio we had that allowed all the family to listen at one time, instead of having to take turns with a headset.

When the man finished his speech, my father turned off the radio, turned around and said to my mother, "Well, I'm going to vote for Roosevelt. Hoover isn't going to help the farmer!"

In 1992, sixty years later, the country was again in deep trouble. We then witnessed the power of television, and we had three choices. Republican Bush, Democrat Clinton and Independent Perot. It was thought possible Perot could say the right thing that night and become our first NOTA (None Of the Above) president. Now, in the year

2000 we again face another presidential election. will high technology computer world open up new problems and possibilities?

November 15, 2000 . . . I think this question is being answered today while some judge in Florida is trying to decide who's going to be our next president. This election between Gush and Bore (I mean Gore and Bush) will go down in history.

CHICKEN PLUCKIN' A DEPRESSION STORY

It was 1933, and Thad, my oldest brother, had graduated from high school. Mom and Dad were both college graduates and education was very important to them. Farm produce was at its lowest price and the future for farmers looked pretty grim. We did have plenty of food to eat and share with friends and relatives in town, but clothes and transportation were a big problem.

The 1928 Chevy with the squeaky brakes would have to transport Don and me to high school and Thad to college. There were two college options—a real highly credited college in Tarkio, Missouri, twenty-three miles south of Shenandoah, or the free Junior College in Clarinda, twenty miles east.

Mom got out her pencil and a piece of paper and she and Dad and Thad all tried to figure how to raise the needed money. Finally, they had a plan. If they could raise 3,000 baby chicks up to fryer size and sell them in Shenandoah it would provide the money for the good college. The big hen house would hold the growing fryers, but they would have to build an incubator building to keep the baby chicks warm. The incubator held 300 chicks, so if they started an assembly-line of raising chickens, and selling them on Saturdays in town, there would be enough money.

When the first 300 chicks were fryer size, we set up an assembly line (I mean a dis-assembly line). Each Saturday we got up early, and all worked on the job. My Dad would chop off their heads, My two older brothers dipped them in hot water and plucked them, Mom cut them up, and Willard and I packaged them and helped clean up. We would take them to town and sell them door to door for 50 cents a package.

I only remember filling the incubator building once with 300 chicks that summer. It was profitable but looked like it would have to be an ongoing business. It was a lot of work but the feed cost nothing. There was a surplus of grains that would cost more to transport than you would receive if they were sold. We were burning corn instead of coal in the furnace because a full wagon load of corn would only buy a bushel or two of coal. One farmer sent a load of hogs to Chicago, and got a bill back instead of money. The hogs didn't sell for enough to pay for the freight.

I wasn't in on the financial planning, but now I think a decision was made for Thad to go to the free Clarinda college, and money was spent to send Thad and Don to see the World's Fair in Chicago. John and Edna Gass (Mom's brother and his wife) lived there and invited the boys to come see the big event. When they came back, they were so excited about it, they thought Mom, and I should also go.

THE CHICAGO WORLD'S FAIR 1933

What I remember. This was my first train ride ever. In Mount Pleasant, we were joined by Aunt Ollie, Mom's aunt who taught school. We ate dinner in the Dining Car and I couldn't believe all the silverware, napkins, fancy plates, glassware and being waited on by a gentleman in a black and white uniform.

In Chicago we were met by John and Edna and taken to their apartment. I had never seen "houses" inside a big building. I remember some about the World's Fair—a miniature train which we rode; ferris wheels and a roller coaster which we didn't ride. Uncle John said they were too dangerous.

The City of Chicago is what I remember most. The Woolsworth Five and Dime Store; riding in an elevator clear to the top of the 48 story building and looking down at the miniature cars and people.

We went to the Zoo. All the animals I'd only seen in a circus were there, plus other animals I didn't know existed. Lake Michigan was so big you couldn't see the other shore—the biggest body of water I'd ever seen or even dreamed of.

I felt like I had just stepped inside the National Geographic, but in color!

BACK TO SCHOOL

By the end of summer, Thad had been accepted by Tarkio College, but there was not enough money to pay the tuition. So, the first day of school, we traveled 20 miles to Clarinda where the Junior College was. Don and I hated the school. All of our friends and cousins would be going to the Shenandoah high school. When I went home that day, I told my Mother I didn't want to go to high school and I hated the Clarinda school. While we were discussing the first day, there was a knock on the door. A very business-like man said he was from Tarkio College and wanted to talk to Thaddeus and my folks.

He presented Thad with a full math scholarship, and said they had arranged for him to deliver Sunday papers in our area for a steady income. Oh, what joy there was that evening at the dinner table. On his way to college, Thad would drop us at our Grandmother's place at 7 a.m., go on to Tarkio College, 23 miles south of Shenandoah. Then, pick us up around 5 p.m. on his way home.

This would not be the end of our problems in the depression, but it was the end of the chicken venture.

THE TRIP WEST

During the devastating depression, my folks lost our beautiful Iowa farm. My Dad went to visit his Mother in California and found work. In the summer of 1936, when school was out, we left Shenandoah. My Mother and two older brothers, Thad and Don took turns driving with Mom back seat driving when they were at the wheel. I could have helped drive, but Mom didn't know my brothers had taught me how. Willard was only 12, so we sat in the back seat and enjoyed the trip. We would be living with my Grandmother Baker in Hollywood. Except for my father, none of us had been farther west than Omaha, Nebraska, sixty miles from Shenandoah. It was quite an experience seeing mountains and plains that we'd studied about in geography classes.

We stopped in Grover, Colorado, about sixty miles from Denver and stayed at aunt Louise and Ray Lawson's ranch. While there, we took a trip to Pike's Peak to see this wonder we'd read about.

Our next destination was Corning, California where we would visit Mom's brother George Gass, his wife Margaret and four cousins we'd never met. Their home was on an olive ranch. Margaret said I was a special niece because I'd been at their wedding a month before I was born.

HOLLYWOOD

In Hollywood, we moved into the house with my Grandmother Baker, on North Martel Avenue. Soon after our arrival, Aunt Estelle (my Dad's sister) introduced me to Ruth Mary Townsend, who lived down at the end of Martel Avenue. Aunt Estelle knew her grandfather, Dr. Ashley. We did some shopping together and one day rode our bicycles up into the Hollywood Hills. When we got back to her Grandparent's place, I met her brother Ashley. I was sweaty and red in the face from the ride and he was covered with grease from head to foot from working on the old relic car Clark Gable was restoring.

Carole Lombard, a very popular movie star, gave Clark a beat up, old car as a joke at his birthday party. Clark spent a small fortune on that car with high speed engines and new paint jobs. Ash still talks about driving it in the high speed trials on the desert salt flats. It was a real "Hot Rod".

Clark Gable has always been one of my favorite actors and Ash said he was really a great guy. We went to see "Gone with the Wind"—think it was one of the very first four hour movies. It cost 50 cents apiece, but we felt it was worth it, especially since the star was named "Ashley". Movies at that time usually cost a dime, and on certain nights they had "Dish Night" where if you went every week you could eventually have a whole set of dishes. They also had drawings with prizes. One night, they called me and said if I'd been there I would have won $100. That was a fortune in the 30's.

Ashley and Ruth Mary's grandparents, George T. Ashley and Amanda were a wonderful introduction to Hollywood. He was the Hollywood Unitarian Minister, and they lived in the big house that served as a church and parsonage. The story of his life as a Methodist Circuit Rider in the south after the Civil War is told in my book "Other Centuries; Other Stories". Ash and I liked his philosophy, "I'll live 'till I die if I don't get killed!"

With Ash and I it was love at first sight. We just felt comfortable and knew we belonged together.

We soon found out we were born 60 miles apart in Iowa. When Dr. Ashley and Amanda moved to Griswold, Iowa they had one son, John, and three daughters, Mary, Catherine and Ruth. Their daughter Catherine met Merle Townsend, a farmer. They fell in love and married. They lived on the farm Merle's parents Dick and Fannie had homesteaded. Ash was born on May 26, 1919; Ruth Mary on May 18, 1921. They lived on the farm, and Ash started school in Griswold. This was before school buses, so his mother drove him the five miles to school through all kinds of weather.

Ash remembers his Grandma Amanda teaching him how to dig for worms and fish on the Nishnabotna river close by. He recalls asking her, "Grandma, when can we go fishin?" She would always reply, "Well, if I don't die before Wednesday, we'll go fishin' then." He also remembers singing "Twinkle, twinkle little star at his grandfather Ashley's church.

As the family grew, the Townsend grandparents moved to Hemet, California, and the Ashley grandparents moved on to Seattle. During the summer of 1926, Ash remembers moving from the farm, first to Hemet, California and then on to Seattle to live with the Ashley grandparents. Jobs were scarce, and the stress of the times led to his parents divorce.

These were tough times and jobs were hard to find, but Catherine got a job as stewardess on the ocean liners and travelled to the Orient and Alaska. Merle played the organ in theaters for the silent movies, and tried selling real estate and other sales jobs. Over the years, Ash and his sister were boarded out or lived with the Ashley grandparents. His grandfather Ashley was now the minister of the Seattle Unitarian church. Ash's cousins Marian and Katie, Ruth's daughters, also were at his grandparents and in Catholic schools after their parents divorced.

When Ash was fifteen, he went back to Iowa with his father to manage the sale of the Townsend's farm. His father returned to Washington and Ash went to live with his Townsend grandparents in Hemet, California. While there, he was driving produce trucks from Hemet to Los Angeles every other night, attending school every day and helping his grandmother take care of his grandfather who was failing. (not much time for homework). During the Ramona Pageant, held there every year in an open, outdoor theater, he played the part of an Indian, standing on a big boulder up in the hills.

To make extra money during those tough times, he learned to milk rattlesnakes and got $10 an ounce for the venom from a local doctor. He gave up this source of income when a big one struck him. He performed the ritual of cutting and sucking the blood out, and was sick for several days under the doctor's treatment. He still has the scar on his wrist and the cost of the medicines made it a low profit venture.

When, in 1936, his Grandpa Ashley was appointed minister of the Hollywood Unitarian Church, he and his sister moved there.

He had just turned 17 when we met. When we started going together, my family became his. Over the years we kept in touch with the Ashley family, but they all had busy lives, and were not the close knit family mine was. In the fifties, Ash and his cousin Marian's paths would cross again when we moved to Seattle. We spent many weekends camping all over Washington with Marian, Owen Alloway and their family, Robin, Keith and Guy.

When we retired in 1980 and went looking for the Social Security office, we found it in Mount Vernon, Washington, fifteen miles east of Anacortes. Ash was surprised that it was just across the street from the May Pickett house where he boarded, and helped build the house and clear the acreage in his early teens. The house was still there. When we drove by the courthouse, the two big cannons he remembered were still guarding it.

Ruth Mary now lives at Lake Elsinore, California where my great grandparents, the Farnhams, moved when they left Iowa.

Ash and I started going to the Hollywood Congregational Church which had a wonderful youth program with a gymnasium built onto the Sunday school classrooms that would accommodate basket and volley ball games, and later dances. Larry's namesake and godparents, Larry and Barb Kollin were part of that group. We remember beach parties, roller-coaster rides, a Halloween party in a big, unfinished house behind the Trocadero night club, basketball and volleyball games at the church, parties at each other's homes, but the most memorable was the weekend at the mines.

THE GOLD MINES

Larry Kollin's Dad owned some property in the gold mine country in the mountains rising from the Mojave Desert. There were five cabins on it and Larry said there was no reason why we couldn't use the cabins for a week-end holiday. There were sixteen teen-agers, and two chaperones Katie Sander's and Barbara's Scott's single mothers. These mines were located over forty miles from the town of Mojave. When we arrived, we discovered two of the cabins had burned down and "squaters" were living in the other three. Two of the families were gone for a week-end in civilization, but the one family there, opened one of the cabins and invited us to use it. This is where the chaperones and some of the kids slept, and we prepared food. At night we gathered around a campfire in front of the cabin that was circled by logs to sit on. I don't know where all sixteen slept. My brother Don and Ash slept on the front porch of the unopened cabin. Rowena and I slept in our car parked in front. In the middle of the night, it started raining and the porch roof leaked, and a dog was howling. Ash threw his boot at the dog and the dog left, but then it started to really rain. The car door opened and a voice said "Move over". We spent a cold, soggy night together, with Rowena in the back seat. Don, in a more protected part of the porch, slept through the night.

The next day a few of us took a hike up a trail. We became intrigued by the constant sightings of peanut shells on the path. We were more than forty miles from civilization! Finally, at the end of this long trail we saw a little cabin and met the occupants. These two young men were prospecting and mining for gold. When they needed supplies, they walked barefoot down to Mojave and ate peanuts on their way back.

MASONJARITE

A year or so after we moved west, Uncle Harlan (Mom's brother) and his family arrived and it was interesting to hear of their trip across the plains. It was good to see our cousins, Bob and Morton again. Grandpa and Grandma Gass would also move to Hollywood with Phyllis their sister.

As a gift, Harlan brought my folks a large volcanic glass artifact. It was a beautiful clear dark green with little white balls in it about the size and shape of moth balls. He bought it from a roadside stand and was told it was an ancient specimen from volcanoes that were in that area thousands of years ago. The rock was about the size of a big footstool and would sit in front of the house for many years. Occasionally it would be missing a piece that someone had "acquired" while nobody was watching.

As we grew up, married and left home, Dad broke off and gave us a "piece of the rock" as a valued keepsake. The chunk Ash and I had was about the size of a softball with one distinct "moth ball". Over the years our family grew and we became campers with our sons, Larry, Bruce and Ron. While still in California we decided to take up rock hounding under the direction of a friend, Slim Robely, who was a geologist. The boys found quite a collection of geodes, opals and other interesting stones, but never any to compare with the green volcanic rock. Slim was shocked when Bruce and Butch brought him a beautiful specimen of an opal, but as they had been taught, they split it in two to share.

While at Queen Anne high school in Seattle in 1958 or '59, Bruce decided to do an essay on the volcanic rock specimen. He spent hours researching in the library for information in gemstone books. He finally found all about the green volcanic rock and the story behind its origin.

It seems a Mason Jar factory burned down in Kansas and the owners declared bankruptcy. (Mason canning jars, like the original Coca Cola bottles were green). A depression entrepreneur discovered this jewel of a find in a huge mass of melted green glass with white gas bubbles in it. He offered to take on the job of disposing the debris and cleaning up the site for a reasonable fee. After being paid for the job, he broke the glass up into huge hunks, and set up a road stand to sell these unusual "volcanic rocks" to those on their way west.

Ash renamed this treasured specimen "Ma***son***jarite". We still have a "piece of the rock" in our bathroom window. It is so pretty when the sun shines through it, outlining the little moth ball in all its glory. Recently, at an estate sale, I bought an antique blue mason jar. These are some of the strange keepsakes we've collected to remind us of the past, and pass down to our family.

HOLLYWOOD HIGH

Imagine going from a high school in the midwest with about 100 students in each grade to a school that had more than 800 graduating each semester. Instead of one five-story building there was a whole square block of many buildings. The September after moving to Hollywood, I was enrolled as a senior, and would graduate in the big ceremony held at the Hollywood Bowl.

My most memorable teacher there was Mr. Burroughs who taught Chemistry. This was my second learning experience in nutrition. The latest new product on the market was a white, solidified oil advertised as "Easy to digest, will not spoil, and no refrigeration required". This and a soap ad that declared "99% Pure" really irritated him. He pounded on the desk and said "Anything that won't spoil cannot be easily digested! Digestion is spoiling!" and "What do they mean by 99% pure? 99% pure what?" He used cooking and household products such as soda, baking powder, vinegar and other common household products to illustrate lessons and use in lab experiments. It was here I learned the basic chemistry of preparing and cooking food.

HOLLYWOOD IN THE 30'S was an exciting glamour city. We would see stars often as they went about their business. You could stand outside the Trocadero and watch all the famous stars, dressed in their finest after the premier of a major movie. We did this one time when Richard Gass was visiting. After seeing almost every famous movie star in Hollywood, and writing down all their names, Richard said "I wish I could tell the people back home all the stars we've seen tonight!" We were surprised and said "Why can't you?" His reply, "They wouldn't believe me!"

We would sometimes go up on Saturday night, find a parking spot on Hollywood Boulevard, and just people watch. The Christmas parades led by Santa Claus was another opportunity to see all the stars in their finest.

In the late 90's we toured Hollywood. Our nephew, Don Schilling had set up an appointment for us to tour Hollwyood High and see their new museum. A high brick wall with wrought iron barriers surrounds the school and we were admitted by an armed guard who checked to see if we had an appointment. The school buildings look more aged, but the same, and we enjoyed the personalized tour. Hollywood High is still an active high school. We were told it is still a place where young hopefuls go, expecting to be "discovered". Ash found me in the 1937 graduating class picture. Willard's name was on a wall with all the other graduates who gave their lives in World War II. I am glad I lived in Hollywood, but will always remember it as it was in the 30's.

THE CONTINUING WATERMELON SAGA

This started in the late 30's when Ash and I became steadies. My brothers would tease him and one time he complained to me if they didn't stop teasing him he might deck one of them. I told him "Hey, if they didn't like you they wouldn't pass the time of day with you!" So, he learned to tease and became a part of our family. Watermelon was a favorite dessert during the summer, and always somebody would complain about the seeds. One day Ash made the statement that in Russia they had seedless watermelons. Nobody believed him and so the in-house joke became seedless watermelons. When unsuspecting guests said something about the seeds, the whole family, in on the joke, would laugh. In 1958 during a family picnic at Thad and Shirley's, it was decided to write letters to Ash who was working in Alaska. When we sent the letters to him, the boys included a BB-cartridge holder filled with watermelon seeds and a string on the end. It looked like a huge firecracker.

The following are just a few of the letters in the 16 pages of watermelon jokes, cartoons and correspondence over the years. Our house has watermelon baskets, pillows, candles and other memorabilia given to us over the years. Marjorie, Thad's daughter and Kathryn, our granddaughter are two that are still involved in carrying on this family tradition. Marjorie has some paintings she did and probably more memorabilia than we have.

A few of the letters:

> Dear Sir: I prefer seedless watermelons to Albino watermelons like my aunt buys (I had bought a watermelon once that was completely white inside—but it had seeds) but I don't understand where they get the seeds to plant the seedless watermelons. Oh! and by the way, which comes first the seeds or the watermelon? Miss M. Baker

> Dear Sir: In regards to the Famous Seedless Watermelon, as far as I am concerned I can truthfully say they are "out of this world!". Yours Truly, Helen Baker

I used to sleep too soundly at night until I tried eating inner Mongolian Seedless watermelon before going to bed. Now I get up four or five times a night just thinking about how they get the seeds to plant the watermelon, which takes you back to the old saying "which came first, the seed or the watermelon." If you have the answer to this question, please let me know. Very truly yours, Al K. Seedzer.

This is an account of the family's activities today at Thad & Shirley's Fourth of July picnic. The whole family, to a man, woman, boy, girl, dog and cat is now making or recently has made a testimonial to Inner Mongolian Seedless Watermelons. Yours truly, Boulder Baker

Dear Sir: I like Inner Mongolian Seedless Watermelons because arf! arf!, bow wow! woof! arf! Yours truly, Man's best friend, Sam

Now, into the 21st century, the saga still goes on, and on and on.

THE YEAR OF THE WEDDINGS

It was the year 1939. My folks would be fazing out having the four of us around to feed, clothe and worry about as we spread our wings. During that year, I would be 19, Willard 15, Thad 23 and Don 21. Thad and Don were working as tellers in banks. I was working at Title Insurance and Trust Company with my friend Shirley Watson. Don and Rowena Walker had been going steady almost as long as Ash and I. Thad had been dating Shirley since they met at a teen party at our home in Hollywood six months before.

When Ash got settled in a good, steady job at Douglas Aircraft, we decided to get married after three and a half years of "going steady". It was popular then to go to Las Vegas, but the car Ash had wasn't ready for a long trip like that, so when he asked my Dad and Mother for my hand, he also asked if we could borrow their car for the week-end.

They looked at each other with a smile on their faces and Dad said "I don't see how we could say 'No' Helen, do you?" Plans were made for the next weekend. The look they exchanged that day always puzzled me. It was like they had a secret, or maybe it was just a sigh of relief to get me married off.

We pooled all our savings, as I remember it was $34 for the trip, and Ash had bought a wedding ring for me . It had a ring of tiny diamonds. Except for being stalled out in the middle of the desert, when Ash accidentally turned off the motor when his knee hit the switch, we had an uneventful trip; got our $2 license at the courthouse and went to a preacher's home for the marriage ceremony. We didn't have the required witness, so he called to his wife and she filled in.

The following June, we would drive Thad and Shirley over for the same trip and $2 wedding license. This time we would be the witnesses. The following September, Don and Rowena would tie the knot at a formal wedding in the Hollywood Congregational Church.

Then Willard went into the Navy Air Force from high school, and the folks were empty-nesters. Both worked in the defense industries supporting the country during the terrible World War II years. Willard would not return from that war.

When my Mother was 90 years old, we visited her in Glendale. My Father died at the age of 84, and she was living alone. I found a box of old photos and keepsakes she had in the bedroom we were in and she and I had fun going through them, discussing old times, and identifying forgotten faces. Then, she pulled out a newspaper clipping and with that same grin I remembered, handed it to me. It said, "Eugene Baker and Helen Gass borrowed his father's automobile, eloped, and were married in Clarinda, Iowa, June 29, 1914.

CHAPTER V

Stories of the 40's WWII & POSTWAR YEARS

We would spend our first anniversary (September 30th, 1940) in Des Moines, Washington. Ash had been offered an opportunity to work at Boeing Aircraft, and we were invited to live at the summer place of a family Ash had boarded with when, as a teenager, he lived in Seattle. At this time, they were teachers of, and boarded, problem children. The children were called "State Wards". This was before "Foster Homes". We managed their 2-1/2 acre lodge, the children and the 6 cabins where the children slept, while they went on a needed two weeks vacation. When school started, they all moved back to their big house in Seattle.

This was my first encounter with a wood stove. Our house on the farm had a modern kerosene stove; the house in Hollywood had a very modern electric stove. This monster had a water tank, an oven and a flat top for cooking. There was also a warming oven above the stove top. The woodshed had various types of wood. This pile was for baking cakes, and using the oven—it burned slow and steady. This pile was for heating something on the stove top. It burned hot and quick, and if you wanted to make donuts or something like that you used the dry grass twigs that really burned hot! Also, you could put the pot on an opened burner by removing the plate and get quick, hot heat for boiling water or making coffee. All this overwhelmed this dummy who hadn't really learned to cook on a regular stove!

It was an interesting three months due to the fact that Boeing went on strike, and the job was not available. We registered with the unemployment office, but checks had to come from California, and there were no jobs available of any kind. We went for ten weeks on what little savings we had, luckily we had no rent to pay and the acreage provided some food. When 10 unemployment checks came in for $17 each, and Boeing was still on strike, we decided it would be wise to head back to California where at least we could get work.

We stopped in Corning, California on our way back and started a lifelong friendship with my Aunt Margaret and Uncle George Gass and their family—Connor, Margaretta, Nathalie Ann and Sandy (George Sanford). As we traveled back and forth from Washington to California over the years, they watched our family grow. They would become very special people in our lives. Sandy was just five years old, and became very interested in the camera Ash had. We felt completely at ease letting him hold it and explore it. He and Ash had quite a conversation about films, printing and developing pictures. I couldn't believe at five the questions he asked. In DesMoines, we had lived next door to a five year old boy, and his three year old sister, and hid all breakables when they came to visit.

THE WAR YEARS 1941–1945

Some despaired, but most did not. A strange sense of humor developed among the survivors that still prevails in our generation today. People worked together, helped each other, worked toward a future for their children. Like the depression, in great crisis, a spirit of togetherness prevails and monumental tasks can be accomplished.

The war years tore at our hearts, but there was also a feeling of a whole nation working together to defeat a terrible enemy. Now with our modern communications; television, movies and political re-hashing of history we are disillusioned by all the horrors that continue in the world. Modern communications will change things in the future—whether for good or bad, will have to be resolved in the future.

All the family were involved in the war—Mom and Dad (Grandpa Eugene and Grandma Helen) were working at Northrup Aircraft, and were written up in the Northrup newspaper for coming back to work the day after receiving the terrible notice of Willard's death on

Leyte. Thad and Don were in the service; Ash was working long hours at the shipyards building Liberty ships. If you haven't lived through it, it is hard to understand the experience of war whether on the battlefront or at home.

I have often wondered if the world reputation the U.S. has had since the Revolutionary War, of everyone hiding behind a tree with a gun is what has kept us from being invaded. In almost every country that was invaded and conquered by Germany, the guns owned by the civilians were first confiscated. The 40s were scary, sad years, but when you are caught up in something like that you live your life the best you know how. If you survive, you go on and put the pieces of your life back together again.

PEARL HARBOR DAY– DECEMBER 7, 1941

In our writing class at the Senior Center in Anacortes, we were asked to write about a happening in our life, placed at a different location; happening to a different person, or written by someone else about you. This was what I wrote in 1995.

It was so quiet this bright Sunday morning—why do the hospitals always wake you up so early for breakfast! Today, Lawerence Ashley Townsend and I would go home. What a big name for such a tiny mite—We'll call him "Larry." In a few hours his father will be here to pick us up and take us home.

I hear planes—a lot of planes! That's odd, they don't usually have so much air activity on Sunday.

Oh, no! It sounds like bombs! Am I dreaming? They must be having maneuvers here in Pearl Harbor. I know a lot of big ships are in the harbor. Usually they publish stuff like that to keep the small boats out of practice areas. But, on Sunday???

The door bursts open. A nurse hands me the baby saying "Pearl Harbor is being bombed by the Japanese! You are on your own. We have been called to emergency stations. The head nurse will still be on duty, but don't call her unless it is a real emergency."

As the door closed, I sat there stunned. What was happening to his father—he was at Hickman Airforce Base? Did we still have a home? What kind of a world were we bringing our firstborn son into? Oh, no, this can't really be happening. It must be just a bad dream!"

THE REAL STORY—Larry was born on November 29th, 1941 at the Santa Monica, California Hospital. I was waiting for his father to come get us. An attendant came in, handed me the baby, and announced "Pearl Harbor has been bombed by the Japanese". The hospital was on alert, not knowing what could happen if the mainland were invaded, so we were told only to use the call button if it was very important. Ash was working at Douglas Aircraft at that time. When he arrived, he hadn't heard the news. We went from the hospital to my folks place in Hollywood. When we brought the first grandchild into the house, everyone was gathered around the radio and said "Shhhh—they're bombing Pearl Harbor". We were sort of surprised that nobody noticed what we had in our arms. Soon the war would become real; blackouts of all lights at night; continuous search lights, and complete dedication by all to fight back!

Two years later, on Pearl Harbor Day December 7, 1943, Bruce would be born at the Osteopathic Temple Hospital in Los Angeles. We were then living in the house on Robinson Street where Don,

Rowena and Virginia lived before the Navy transferred them to Spirit Lake, Idaho. The hospital was on the hill back of this place. The Robelys, Slim, Mary Ellen and Butch (Spencer Hart Robely III) lived across the street. They moved to La Crescenta before their second boy, Boyd was born. Butch was a year younger than Larry. They would enter our lives again in the 50s.

My brother Willard was killed on Leyte . For our family, this was the saddest of many war tragedies. All of Willard's friends had preceded him in giving their lives for their country. My Mother said "Losing a parent or older person is sad, but there are no words to express the hurt of losing one of your children, no matter what age." She would lose her oldest son, Thad when he had a heart attack at forty-three. Don and I would outlive our parents.

Ron was born also at the Temple hospital on September 14th, 1945. The war years and the years after the war were tough years, but there was a spirit of dedication and willingness to sacrifice to end that terrible war. Rationing of sugar, gasoline, shoes, meat and shortages of many other things made life a challenge. One time Mary Ellen and I decided to pool our meat ration stamps and buy a ham. We wanted the butcher to divided it but he said, "No way—you two are friends and I'm not going to break up a friendship by trying to divide a ham equally". So we stayed friends and did the job ourselves—with our families sharing a meal or two together. With three rapidly growing children, shoe rations stamps were the most needed. I was able to trade sugar stamps for shoe stamps.

All three of our boys were born before television, antibiotics, polio shots, frozen foods, plastic, frisbees, pet rocks, hoola hoops, skate boards, radar, credit cards, ball point pens, dishwashers, electric blankets, air conditioning, drip-dry clothing and before man walked on the moon. Rabbits were rabbits; not Volkswagens which weren't introduced yet. They were before fast foods—MacDonalds, Pizza, yogurt or cake mixes. Instant or decaffeinated coffee was unheard of. Five and ten cent stores actually had items for five and ten cents. Ice cream cones were five cents for one scoop; ten cents for two. For a nickel you could ride a street car, make a phone call, buy stamps to mail a letter and two postcards. New cars sold for $600 to $800. Not many people could afford to buy one, and made do with second hand cars for $25 to $150. But, you didn't have to have a mechanic and an electronic technician to fix them. During WWII, margarine was white and had a little capsule of coloring you had to mix into it. The challenge during the war was "Have you learned to eat margarine white yet?"

When the war ended, the blackout of lights was lifted, and driving through Hollywood one night, we wondered what all the excitement was about in the back seat. When we saw the boys looking at all the lights, we realized they had never seen neon or street lights before. We took a drive around the busy streets just admiring the displays we hadn't seen for four years. It was sort of like Christmas, and made us realize the war really was over.

After the war was over, the shipyards closed. Welders and many others were out of work. Ash worked for a while at a photo shop in Hollywood and when his father needed help after a major heart operation, we left for Summit View a small community between Puyallup and Tacoma, Washington. In a few months his father recovered. We were doing door to door photography with a speed graphic camera, taking baby pictures, family, wedding and school pictures. From there we decided to move to eastern Washington, and ended up in a cabin on Liberty Lake, east of Spokane.

SUMMIT VIEW, SPOKANE AND LIBERTY LAKE

It was shortly after World War II when we decided to pack up our dreams and our photographic equipment to seek the fortune we were sure awaited us in the Northwest. We packed all our dishes, pots and pans, bedding and clothes inside the old 1936 Packard. On the top rack we added various photographic equipment, including a huge enlarger. As we said 'good-bye' to our families, my brother, Thad, said, "You kids look like the last chapter of the Grapes of Wrath."

In spite of all the dire predictions of friends and families, we did arrive in Washington. Settled, for the time being, in a little community five miles between Tacoma and Puyallup, where we started in earnest to earn our living with the camera.

Our first order was from a sign painter. We traded for a sign that read:

PHOTOGRAPHY

Commercial, Aerial Weddings and Home Portraits

It was rather pretentious for the small community and our limited equipment, but it was impressive.

Business was slow at first, and Ash's knuckles were becoming calloused from knocking on doors. There were more offers to trade than to buy. A group picture of a music class netted twelve lessons and a guitar, which we didn't need; a family group picture resulted in a tune-up for the old Packard, which it did need; baby pictures brought very little cash but many chickens, rabbits and home-canned goods, which at least were edible.

The weather was gloomy and wet, and the washroom was doing double duty as a darkroom by night and laundry by day. An endless procession of babies, animals, families and weddings marched across the easel in the darkroom, into the trays of developer, hypo, water, dryer and into the hearts of countless grandmothers, parents, family, friends and lovers. We never tired of watching the different faces appear in the developing tray. We never saw a small child's hands caught in an ungraceful pose; or any adult's in a graceful pose. It was always exciting to see how pleased the customers were with the pictures they wanted so much—pictures that couldn't be duplicated in a studio. I remember the picture of the little boy pounding a nail into a block of wood. It brought tears to his mother's eyes, because it didn't show the vacant look in his; the little German woman who just couldn't understand how I had colored her daughter's arm under the filmy wedding veil; the wedding pictures that had to be re-taken because of a mechanical failure in the camera shutter; the unshed tears of frustration spent in finding and fixing the ailing camera (Ash went back the next morning at 7:30 to get them out of bed and re-take the pictures because he knew they were leaving early that morning); the woman who brought her cocker spaniel twenty miles to have his picture taken on a three-wheeled kiddie kar; the picture of the Grange dance band, led by the drummer who was also the school bus driver, janitor, owner of the local feed and grain store, and supervisor of the weekly boxing matches. The dance always lasted until about two o'clock in the morning when he fell off his chair or his wife who owned and operated the Grange coffee and cookie concession ran out of cookies. Then there was the blonde woman who wanted a real glamour pose, but could only find a pin saying "Mother" to fasten the draped, off-the-shoulder gown; the babies who would laugh at anything, and the sober ones who would laugh at nothing; and the little boy who said "Gee, you got a camera just like the one Hypo has in Dick Tracy."

By Christmas of that year, we were beginning to dream again of the fortune we had envisioned, but after Christmas, business was slow. We depended almost entirely on our traded merchandise and waited for spring. In April, the country emerged from its winter cocoon, and we had our first order for school pictures. A new door had opened. Two weeks later we delivered two hundred and twenty group pictures of grinning, tousle-headed kids of all ages, and pocketed more than a hundred dollars.

The rabbits in their hutches were getting fat, and the garden ready to produce some tender, fresh vegetables the day Ash came home with eyes sparkling. "Honey, we're moving on to Spokane. At the photo shop I met a fellow from there. He said he was here to get away from all the people who wanted baby pictures taken." Again, it was time to move on. Ash's father had recovered from his operation and his family, Louise and their daughters Merline (9) and Sharon (7), would probably like to get back to their quiet life.

We removed our sign, packed up our belongings, and with few regrets headed east. We found a quaint, almost primitive cabin on a beautiful lake, sixteen miles from Spokane and decided this would be our home and workshop while we located all the mothers who wanted pictures of their little ones.

We obtained contracts for more school pictures, and although the number of hours spent were many for the money made, there was a great satisfaction in this work. The trend in school pictures was to individual, posed portraits rather than the old-fashioned group pictures, and we knew the pictures we took of groups would be some of the last of their kind. Just as the old pitchur pump with the long-handled dipper and the rope-pulled bell in the steeple of the one-room school houses had been replaced with the modern, consolidated schools with drinking fountains and electric bells, so would the informal group pictures be replaced by commercial portraits.

We never did find all the mothers who were clamoring for pictures of their children, but a commercial, traveling photo lab from Denver, Colorado with a big advertising campaign, many solicitors and free introductory offers did. More and more we became aware of the constant struggle between the old and the new. The old wood stove, with the firewalls wearing thin, seemed to chide us for using presto logs. We resented its pokiness, yet enjoyed its warmth. Must warmth always be sacrificed for efficiency? To compete with the new, we needed modern, automatically controlled equipment, but with the new would come the loss of the warm, personal contact. The pictures would become just pieces of paper.

Here we were, over a thousand miles from our "roots" in Los Angeles, with three boys—Ron turned two while we were at Liberty Lake. The day after his birthday, Bruce looked at him and said "Yesterday he was one year old. Now he is two?" We assured him this was so. Then he said "Well, he doesn't look any different!"

For Opening Day, Ash bought Larry a fifteen cent bobber, tied it to a string on a stick, and showed him how to dig for worms and put them on the hook. At six, Larry had the patience to sit quietly among the men who lined the lake with their expensive rigs. We were watching from the cabin, and all of a sudden saw a group of the fishermen crowding around Larry. At first we thought he might have fallen in the lake, but then saw they were all helping him land a really big one. Now he became the star, and they were all asking him what he was using for bait. Later, we saw grown men digging for worms. It turned out that his fish was the largest caught that day and Larry was written up in the local paper. We met some interesting people that summer. Bud and Kenny—two teen agers who invaded the resort every weekend, and provided entertainment for the boys and visions for us of what we would experience when our boys became teenagers. Larry did a lot of fishing, but never caught another big one.

The last few months we were at Liberty Lake, we got acquainted and started working with a couple who took pony pictures. This was a new door opening up to explore, but when the winter winds blew across the lake through the cracks in the cabin walls, and we had to set hot-water bottles under the developing trays to keep the solutions at working temperature, we decided it was time to return to California and the world of tomorrow.

SAY GOOD-BYE TO THE PICTURE MAN

The little girl's mother lifted her off the piano stool and straightened the dainty, pink organdy dress. "Say 'Good-bye' to the picture man, Betty"

Betty gave us her first smile of a grueling half-hour sitting, but it was too late. The camera was packed away.

The mother's words echoed in my mind, for this truly was good-bye to the picture man. Not just this picture man, but to all the itinerant photographers who have roamed this country since the invention of the camera. For us, it was good-bye to our nomadic life with a camera.

We would never forget this happy, eventful detour in our lives. We feel a deep satisfaction in the knowledge that we were one of the last of the itinerate photographers. We also feel a twinge of regret that our children and their children, born to this modern, electronic age, will never have such natural, unposed pictures of their schoolmates. At the turn of the new century 2000 the photo technology has exploded with digital cameras that don't use film, and can be immediately shown or sent by e-mail to the family. Our high tech photography is intriguing, and will put new aspects on the art. Much of it will be better.

When Betty's mother told her to "Say Good-bye to the picture man," I'm sure she didn't realize what a profound statement she had made.

WHERE DO WE GO WHEN WE GO TO SLEEP—Bruce was four and did not understand distances involved when we moved to Liberty Lake. He woke up one night and in a sleepy voice said "Mama, where do we go when we go to sleep?" He had dreamed of his beloved Grandma Helen and his cousins in California. Have you ever tried to explain dreams or how far 1,000 miles is to a four-year-old in the middle of the night?

Over the years that question has re-occurred to me after any number of dreams. Many books have been written about dreams, out-of-the-body experiences, nightmares and their meanings. Throughout history there have been stories of "visions", ghost appearances, spirits and poltergeists.

Many years later, after a strange, out of the body experience I would wonder ***"Where DO we go when we go to sleep".***

RACIAL TOLERANCE

My Grandma Gass hired a Negro maid and the following story was told many times. She laughed and told my grandmother about my brother Don, who was about four years old. One day he came into the kitchen where she was working, and very quietly came up to her, wet his finger and touched her arm. When she turned around, he was in a corner looking at his finger to see if the black came off. In our part of Iowa, there were very few people of color. In school, of course, we learned the history of the slaves and the civil war that freed them. During the late 20th century, I recently learned that the word "Negro" is not now considered acceptable. We were taught that it was a very respectful word for the black people. "Nigger", like "White Trash" and "Shanty Irish" was not. Ash's Grandmother Amanda Ashley from the south called them "Nigrah". Her best friend as a child was a slave girl and she loved the people of color.

We have known some very dear black Americans, and have known some that were not. This holds true of every person I've ever met. The color of their skin, whether they were tall or short, skinny or fat had nothing to do with my feelings toward them. To me how a person is treated usually depends on their actions. The following is a story that expresses more how I feel it should be.

Shortly after returning to California from our venture in Washington, my father, Grandpa Eugene, received a telegram that his mother (in her late nineties) was ill. The boys and I took him to the Los Angeles train station to go to her side in Colorado. We entered the busy terminal with hundreds of people heading in all directions. Dad carried Ron, the little one, and Bruce and Larry held onto my hands. The station was big and the loud speakers were giving directions to train 23 on track 17; train 27 on track 15 and on and on. Then we heard "Train 22 on track 18" leaving for Denver in 32 minutes". With more walking, we finally found the train to Denver.

I told Larry to watch after his two brothers and stay right there while I got Grandpa to his seat on the train. All went well and I got Dad settled for the long trip ahead.

When I came out of the train, the boys were standing just as I had left them. A uniformed Porter was standing at the foot of the steps. He said, "Mam, are these your boys?" I replied, "Yes, have they been doing something wrong?" He said, "No, but they just keep staring at me?"

My mind went into a tailspin! Had they ever seen a black man up close? Hadn't they seen pictures in their books? This was before TV (at least in our family). I recalled my childhood with the phonograph and radio—the Two Black Crows, and similar character roles, and of course books like "Little Black Sambo". I took a deep breath, and asked the boys if something was wrong, and why they were staring at the porter. I held my breath. Larry, who decided to be the spokesman, said "Nothings wrong. We're just waiting for him to say 'ALL ABOARD'."

Then the loud speakers rang out "Train 22 to Denver, leaving on Track 18" in three minutes. The porter broke out in a big grin, looked carefully up and down the train to make sure nobody was watching, and burst out in a hearty ***"ALL ABOARD"!***

As we left the terminal, the loudspeakers were still blasting their messages, but this little family felt the world was in order, and I know the porter felt the same way. Wouldn't it be nice if racial problems were that simple?

CHAPTER VI

OUR LIFE IN THE 50's

We came back to California; spent some time trying to do the pony picture business. Dinky, the pony we rented from a stable had been trained for pony picture work. Ash soon found out if he didn't give him a real workout when he picked him up, and give him some bubble gum, Dinky would escape sometime during the day. One day in the middle of Hollywood, he did run away, and was heading for busy Sunset Boulevard. Ash borrowed a bicycle from a neighbor boy and chased after him, catching him just before he ran out into the traffic. We had a nice cowboy hat and it looked like the business could be a success. Dinky was nicely marked; very small—only 36 inches from ground to the small of his back. We were told he came within an inch of being the world's smallest Shetland pony for the Guinness records. When a child was put upon his back and Ash got the camera set up, he would snap his fingers and Dinky would put his front feet together, perk up his ears and pose. When he heard the click of the camera, he would slump down again. Ash would tell him to show a kid his bubble gum and he would work his mouth around so it would show. He chewed it all day long. About this time the Polaroid camera came out and we thought it would be a real winner to be able to deliver on the spot. Not so! People did not trust the new polaroid because the pictures were already brown.

So, another detour. Ash answered an ad for a sales job with a promising non-profit health insurance company. His area would be in San Bernardino and Riverside counties east of Los Angeles.

CRESTLINE

In September, 1950, we moved to Crestline, a small resort village in the San Bernardino mountains. At five, seven and nine (before we had television) the boys were into reading and listening to Hansel and Gretel, Little Black Sambo and other fairy tales. Grandma Kay had read them the scary story of Hansel and Gretel shortly before we moved.

The 120 mile trip from Hollywood to the mountains above San Bernardino was an adventure for all of us, but when we got in sight of the forest we realized Bruce at seven was not taking any chances. He was methodically breaking off pieces of bread and throwing them out the window just like Hansel and Gretel did so they could find their way out of the forest.

It was Labor Day Weekend and the area was very busy and crowded but we managed to get settled in the small mountain cabin with a sleeping loft Ash had rented. It had a sign over the front door "Ye Olde Step Inn" The cabin was in the Valley of Enchantment with a small general store, riding stables, and after Labor Day, mostly unoccupied summer cabins. Larry soon learned to ride a horse for helping at the stables.

We celebrated Ron's fifth birthday and Bruce and Larry experienced their first bus ride to the school up on the ridge above the main part of Crestline. It was a mile and a half up to the ridge. They soon found out that if they missed the bus it was a long walk because their Dad had already left for his job in San Bernardino. Ron was busy exploring the neighborhood—they didn't have kindergarten there at that time.

We were only in that cabin a few months because locals warned us when winter came we would not be able to get out because of deep snow. We found another place on the main road—a two story house with a garage down below, on the highway. We got acquainted with the telephone man, Todd Dasch, who installed our telephone. He and his wife Berniece lived two door on down the road. They had a little black dog Berniece called "Snowball" because she found her abandoned in a snow bank.

One day Ron came marching home and announced that the little black, long-legged pup he had on a leash had been given to him by a lady down the road. We all fell in love with the little fellow and later learned he was a thoroughbred miniature Schnauzer with papers. As he grew, we figured he had been given to Ron because, of the litter, he was the only one with long legs (a throwback into the standard line), or so they said. We never bothered to apply for his papers.

The boys named him Little Black Sambo. He was timid, not too smart, but a faithful family dog who kept other pets that little boys accumulate (white mice, rats and other fuzzy animals) ecologically in balance. The first time he barked, it scared him so he came running inside and hid.

Larry taught Snowball a lot of tricks when she came over to play with the boys. One day Berniece called and asked if she was there. I said "Yea, do you want to talk to her", and held the phone down to Snowball's ear. Berniece said "Snowball, you come home". She went immediately to the door to be let out. After that, if the phone rang while she was there she would look up to see if it was for her.

I became a Den Mother for the Cub Scout troop, which included a set of identical twins. It was an active Boy Scout community, but most who lived there were very poor and couldn't afford proper uniforms. The Scout Masters got special permission to not require uniforms. They had one full outfit, and when they had to send a representative to a regional awards affair, whichever boy fit the uniform was the one chosen. Larry had the honor the year we were there.

One of their major events (this was back in 1950) was a Minstrel Show. We never dreamed at that time that minstrel shows or the name "Little Black Sambo" would be considered politically incorrect, or that there would ever be such a term.

The twins, dressed in costume tuxedos, sang "Me and My Shadow", each standing on one side of a large framed mirror that had no glass. Larry would have Snowball do her tricks. All went well at the rehearsals, but when Snowball came out on the stage that night, she did not recognize Larry with a black face, so she just stood there looking at the audience who were clapping and laughing when she was introduced as "Snowball".

Larry, frantically tried to get her attention. Finally, she recognized his voice and went through her routine. The audience clapped and cheered and she liked that. They had a hard time convincing her the act was over and finally Larry had to carry her off the stage.

Little Black Sambo's nickname was just SAM. He would be part of our family for many years and many more detours.

AN ENCOUNTER WITH OUR LEGAL SYSTEM

American Independent Medical (AIM) paid the doctors and hospitals direct. It was quite well-accepted and Ash was promoted to Regional Supervisor, making good money with a high career potential. One day we were waiting for the boys to come home from school so we could go to Los Angeles for Thanksgiving. There were simultaneous knocks on the front and back doors, and we were invaded by a Sheriff with a drawn gun, and a state insurance representative. They demanded all of the money Ash had on him; confiscated all the company records and tried to take my typewriter, but I finally convinced them it did not belong to the company.

After the shock of it, we asked them what would have happened if we had already left for Los Angeles. They said they had the description and license number, of our car and would have stopped us. Later we would find out they had also confiscated our Post Office Box, and opened all our mail. This was our own personal box;

not a company box. We began to realize what it must have been like in Germany when the Gestapo were allowed to raid your home at any time. When they left they put a notice on our door. About a half hour later, the Sheriff came back and with an apology, suggested that if "the wind blew the notice away" he would not notice.

Later we were told that the major competition had filed a complaint with the State Insurance Commission because AIM offered to pay for X-rays. They claimed that was acting as an insurance company; not as a non-profit. Anyway, while it was tied up in court, Ash would have no job. In San Bernardino, he applied and was accepted as a Life Insurance salesman. Hard work with no career potential, but it would provide our financial needs. Another detour!

SAN BERNARDINO

After spending winter in the Valley of Enchantment, we learned what they meant about the snow. Even with the main highway being cleared with snowplows, working in San Bernardino was not practical. A couple of months after school started the next year, we moved down the hill to San Bernardino. Our first house there would be just across the road from the main railroad that passed through town. We finally got used to the noise and didn't even try to straighten the pictures on the wall. After a couple of weeks, Casey Jones who came through at 5 a.m. blowing his horn, didn't even wake us.

The first day of school was traumatic. I had walked the boys to the school to register them, about eight or ten blocks, and did not think it necessary to pick them up. In the mountains they hiked all over and school there was more than a mile from home. Bruce arrived home late, and was really upset. Apparently his sense of direction had crossed him up, but he had eventually found his way home. Ron had apparently headed the wrong direction. I went to the phone to report to the police, but before I dialed I saw a police car driving by the house. I ran out to flag him down, but he had turned the corner. I just picked up the receiver to call again, saw the police car and rushed out in time to stop him. As I got near the car, I saw the top of a familiar blond head just visible in the window. The policeman was real angry with me, until he found out Ron was in first grade and it was his first day in the new school. With his little round face, he looked much younger. He had remembered the house was near the big Langendorf bakery and the railroad tracks.

We found a better rental later, just across from the school and moved there. The first night there, Bruce fell out of the upper bunk and broke his arm at 2 a.m. At the hospital, Ash and I were given the third degree, and the doctor who was supposed to be on duty wouldn't come down until all X-rays, etc. were taken. Ash knew the head doctor at the hospital and asked them to call him. The doctor arrived in a matter of minutes with his pajama tops tucked into his pants. He went to work, setting the broken bone under a fluoroscope. When Bruce whimpered a little as he was setting it, the doctor said "I guess maybe we'd better put him under anesthetic". Bruce's answer was "No, that's all right. I just wasn't used to it yet." The doctor shook his head, smiled, and continued the job.

Two weeks later, Ron, standing behind Larry when he was trying out a golf club, ended up requiring a bunch of stitches on his forehead. One nurse stopped another while she was carrying Ron, and said "Remember the little boy who came in with the broken arm at two in the morning? Well, this is his brother".

With all three boys in school, I went to work for the dairy and later a real estate/insurance office part time. One afternoon we got a note from the Principal to come over about a problem. It seemed that on the day the police were to arrive at the school to question about a vandalism act, Larry and his buddy had not shown up at school. We hadn't heard about the vandalism, but found out that it had happened over the weekend while we were in Los Angeles. After quite a "discussion" with Larry, we found out his buddy's older brother and friends were the culprits. Larry and his friend knew all about it, but were afraid to say anything for fear they would be in trouble with the "gang". I don't know what happened to the culprits, but Larry was off the hook, and we would soon move down to the other end of that street to our last residence in San Bernardino.

The boys were all members now of the YMCA; would sell soap door to door to earn money to go to camp. I thought they would all go together, but Larry and Bruce were sent to Catalina Island, and Ron up in the mountains. They, I am sure, have stories of that experience. All I remember is getting letters—one said "I had to write this before they would give me breakfast". I also remember Ron arriving back home in the same clothes he left in, with a soggy, moldy suitcase full of clothes. It rained the first night he was there and the tent leaked.

Ash would go back into welding, and in the summer of 1954 he had a job in Haines, Alaska welding the storage tanks for oil lines from northern Alaska.

We had decided to move back to the L.A. area, so when school was out we moved into Grandma Kay and Ruth Mary's apartment for a month or so to wait for Ash's return. Ruth Mary came out and helped us move, after we had sold most of our furniture. What we didn't sell was given to a company that gave us a receipt for all the items to be held on consignment. Later, we would find out the receipt had an address on it that did not and never had existed.

A bit of history—The first McDonald's hamburger stand was in San Bernardino—we were there when they had a sign up announcing they'd sold one million hamburgers.

SUNLAND/ TUJUNGA 1955

When Ash returned from Alaska, we moved to a rental home in Sunland nestled in the foothills north of Glendale. There we would meet the Switzers who would become lifelong friends. Also, we would be closer to all our family. Thad, Shirley, Carolyn and Marjie lived in LaCrescenta.

(The family all called it Rockacenta). Also, Slim and Mary Ellen Robely, long time friends from Robinson Street in L.A. during the 40's, lived in LaCrescenta. They now had four boys—Butch, Boyd, Brian and Barry. They also had a big Collie named "Bruce". They said they had picked the name of Bruce for one of their boys, but we beat them to it. When with them, it was "Bruce boy" or "Bruce dog". Glendale, where my folks, and Don and Rowena's family lived was only 15 to 20 miles away.

Ron and Al Switzer a neighbor would become life-long buddies. One day Ash and I heard a knock at the door. When we opened the door there stood the cutest little girl, dressed in patent leather shoes, a pretty dress, a bonnet and white gloves. She said "I've come to call". We invited her in and got acquainted over cookies and milk. She said she lived two doors down and Ron was a friend of her brothers. Later, we would meet her parents—When Dick saw Ash shoot a gofer in our yard, he came down and congratulated Ash on joining the Gofer Gitters Club.

Dick was a fire chief in what was called the Tujunga/Sunland district, the Foothill Boulevard community. Marian came to call and said Sandy had come home all excited and said "Oh, Mom, I've found some new friends."

We settled down here for a few years—Ron joined the Cub Scouts; Bruce the Young Democrats and Larry the Sea Scouts. We would soon buy (put a down payment on) a house in the foothills south of the town of Tujunga, just a couple of miles from Sunland in the same school district. There we would meet George and Francie Stephenson and their little ones, Mike and DeeDee who lived behind our new home.

First we bought a new VW bug which was an experience in itself. How we could get the three boys, now nearing their early teens, the dog and camping gear into that little car, I'll never know. After one rollover which almost totaled the bug, didn't hurt anyone, or break any glass, we ordered a new red and white Volkswagen Kombi camper. When it arrived, it was a yellow city utility color.

If we refused delivery, we would have to wait another six months, so we took it. The boys named it "Old Yaller". About that time there was a popular toothpaste ad "Wonder Where the Yellow Went?" The boys put a sign on it saying "This is where the Yellow went". With the hard-earned money Ash brought home from Alaska, we invested in complete camping gear to go with Old Yaller and spent many weekends enjoying the desert and mountains collecting rock specimens. Slim was a geologist and taught us all about which rocks were worth finding on our camping trips.

OUR FIRST CAMPING TRIP

Our first camping trip with the new VW Kombi would be to the Mojave Desert. Slim, Mary Ellen and their four boys would join us. The seven boys ranged in age from Larry at 14 down to Barry about 2 years of age. We found a nice spot along a small stream with bushy foliage and small trees. In a clear area, we finally figured out how to pitch the big tent. The boys decided to be real brave and were all going to sleep in a pup tent with the dogs—the Collie, Bruce and our dog Sam. We had forgotten to put in a table of any kind, so Mary Ellen and I were cooking on our knees while Brian and Barry ran circles around our cooking area. The older boys and the dogs were off exploring the creek. Slim and Ash were finishing up getting the tent in order. When dinner was served, one of the boys said "Why did you put sand in the chicken and dumplings"?

By the time it was dark, we were all settled in and everything was quiet. About two a.m. there was an awful commotion outside, dogs barking, kids yelling and a truck driver on the road above honking, yelling and cursing! When we got out of the tent we saw a bunch of range cows running up toward the road with the dogs barking at them. One of the range cows had poked its head in the pup tent and the dogs took over. When the camp was all settled down, we went back to our tents and slept fitfully the rest of the night. The next day we would do some rockhounding.

I had spent most of the week getting prepared and packed for the weekend, and when we got home, it took me most of the week cleaning up all the camp gear and dishes. By this time the gang was all ready to go again. I then and there set down the rules we lived by from then on. When we left camp, everything would be clean and packed, ready to go on the next trip. This worked out great and we would enjoy many, many trips in California and all over Washington. We also had the rule that when we left camp the area was to be cleaner than we found it.

When I see all the bags of garbage and trash people pick up on our highways, I wonder where this philosophy and practice fell down. ***Ash would spend another summer in 1958, working in King Salmon, Alaska. While he was gone, I took the boys on a camping trip we'll all remember. I won third place in the Santa Clara Valley Writers Conference in 1963 for the following story. I'm sure all the boys, including Richard have their own versions, but this was mine.***

ROUND SQUARE IN A PEG HOLE

I tossed the last sleeping bag into the back compartment of "Old Yaller" our Volkswagen bus and tried to ignore the sense of anxiety that urged me to abandon this camping trip. But, a promise is a promise, and even though their father was working in Alaska, I decided to take the three boys camping.

I closed the compartment door and gave our usual signal for take-off, "Wagons Ho-o-o-o." Three blond, blue-eyed boys erupted from the house, carrying last minute treasures such as books, swim fins, straw hats, a mason jar with holes punched in the lid and a rock hammer for collecting mineral specimens. Close at their heels and first in the car was Sam, our black woolly dog. He never took chances on being left behind.

Just as I climbed into the driver's seat, the phone rang. I was tempted to drive off, leaving it ringing in the vacant house, but it demanded to be answered. It was Mom Kay, my mother-in-law. She was calling from the private school in Ojai where she housemothered a dormitory of twelve lively little boys.

"Honey, do you think you could possibly take care of one of the boys for two weeks?"

"I don't think . . . ," I started to protest.

"His folks are in Alaska and can't be back for two weeks. We just haven't any place to send him and Mr. Burrows suggested I call you. He is the headmaster and you would be paid the same as the school tuition for two weeks. The school closed yesterday," she continued, "and I have to be back in Los Angeles tomorrow."

Again I started to protest, "I just don't see how . . ."

"He's such a sweet boy." To her, I thought, they were all little angels.

"He's eight years old and I thought it would be so nice for him to be with the boys."

There was no use protesting further. Fate must have made me answer the phone. Anyway, I reasoned, what difference would one more boy make on a camping trip.

"OK, Mom Kay, I guess I can manage. Does he have a sleeping bag? We were just leaving on a camping trip when the phone rang."

"Well, don't worry, we have an extra one here. We'll be by to pick him up as soon as we can get there."

I locked the front door again, tossed in the extra bag, and climbed back into the car.

A chorus of questions greeted me. "What's the other sleeping bag for, Mom?" Ron, our ten-year-old asked.

"It's for another little boy that's going with us."

"What little boy? Is he my age?" This from Bruce who had just turned twelve.

"No," I answered. "He's only eight. It's one of the boys in Grandma Kay's dormitory.

Larry tightened the lid on the mason jar. "Oh, boy. We get to go to the school." At fourteen, he was at the collection age, stamps, rocks, bugs, butterflies. "Sure wish they'd let me ride one of their horses."

The school grounds were deserted and everything strangely quiet as we climbed up the outside stairs of the Spanish-styled pink stucco building and entered the dormitory hall. Our footsteps echoed in the emptiness of the building. At the end of the hall, Grandma Kay sat in the midst of a mound of bed-sheets, pillowcases and towels. Near her, on a bulging suitcase, sat a forlorn little boy with dark hair, soft brown eyes and a pixie face.

Grandma Kay threw her arms around all three boys and said, "Ricky, these are my grandsons. They're going to be your big brothers until your folks get back." She gathered him into the group. "You'll have lots of fun with them."

"Grandma, can we go out to see the horses in the stable?" Larry asked.

"Yes, but you must stay outside the fence."

"What's in the bottle, Larry?" I heard Ricky ask as they raced down the hall and out the rear door.

"Yes", I thought. "What is in that bottle?" It could be anything! I made a mental note to check it before we left.

Mom Kay returned to sorting the laundry and told me what little she knew of the boy. "He came here from a military school in Los Angeles just a couple of months ago". She tossed a grubby towel on the mound of laundry. "I know very little about him except that he was adopted by his grandparents after his father died in a tidal wave fishing boat accident, and his mother died shortly after. He was only five when it happened, so probably doesn't remember too much about it."

She wrote down an address on a piece of paper. "This is his folks' address in Alaska and also their Santa Barbara address in California. Mr. Burrows will let them know about the arrangements."

I picked up the suitcase, tennis racket and sack of miscellaneous junk so familiar to a mother of three sons and went in search of the boys. As we waved good-bye to Grandma Kay, Ricky bounced up and down on the seat. "I've never been in a Volkswagen bus before. I own a Jeep." It seemed he had lost his shyness already.

"Aw, don't be silly, Ricky, you're too young to own any car." one of the boys said.

"Well, I do!

"All right, boys, let's watch for a MacDonald's. We'll get some hamburgers and an ice cream cone." On the outskirts of Ventura, we found a stand and things seemed more peaceful as we continued down the coast. It was not until we were well into the traffic of Los Angeles that Larry shouted, "Where's my Tarantula?"

I clutched the steering wheel and swerved, almost hitting another car. I was sure I felt the creature crawling up my back! So that's what he had in the mason jar!

"You left it at school, Larry." Ricky laughed. "I wonder what Mrs. Kay thinks about that!" I wondered too, but was glad it was her problem now instead of mine. I was sure she would handle it in her usual calm manner and hoped it would be pickled the next time we saw it.

Over the monotonous drum of the motor I could hear the chatter of the boys. "Oh, I don't believe that!" "Big deal!" "Oh sure. I'll just bet you did!"

Laced in with this boy talk, I heard an occasional "wolf, airplane, Jeep, seals," and wondered if all little eight year old boys were prone to telling tall tales, or if this was going to be a real problem during his stay with us. I couldn't remember our boys going through that stage at eight—seemed more like when they were four. I wondered if it might be caused by insecurity and tried to recall what the psychology books said about it. No telling what this little waif had experienced in his tossed about life. Maybe he was just trying to get attention from the bigger boys. Right now, first things first. Psychological musing and problems would just have to wait.

It was now dusk and high time to look for a camping place for the night. We headed toward the beach south of Los Angeles and started tracing down the camps listed on the map. Camp after camp told us they were full; some didn't allow dogs; some just didn't exist (probably swallowed up in the mushrooming suburbs).

It was dark when we finally pulled up at a deserted-looking spot near the beach at San Clemente. I just couldn't drive another mile! I stumbled out of the car and surveyed the beach across the railroad tracks. Four sleepy, grouchy boys tumbled out after me, dragging their sleeping bags, Sam at their heels.

"Is this where we're going to camp?"

"I don't see any tents or anything out there!"

"Is it legal to sleep on the beach just anywhere?"

"I don't care if it's legal or not," I snapped. "This is where we're going to camp tonight!" Did I detect a slight note of hysteria in my voice? As my eyes adjusted to the darkness, I could see a few scattered neon lights blinking in the distance. A few hundred feet down the tracks stood a deserted railroad station. We crossed the tracks and sank to our ankles in the soft sand. We fumbled in the darkness, untying knots and unzipping zippers. I helped Ricky with his. "Is this what we use instead of blankets?"

"Yes, it is," I told him, "and in just two shakes I'll have you zipped up nice and snug."

"Don't we have to wear our pajamas?" He asked.

"Not tonight. Just take your shoes and socks off and keep them inside the sleeping bag so they won't get lost."

Moments later, snuggled down in my own bag, surrounded by four vague lumps in the sand, my mind still whirled with the many thoughts and events of the day just past—was it just one day? The soft sand became harder and harder. I was sure it had turned to cement.

Just as I was drifting off to sleep, the sand started to shake and a flashing light blinded me. A commuter train came barreling down the tracks, roared past us and faded off into the distance. I expected a commotion from the boys, but they never stirred, completely oblivious to the cares of the world. I felt something crawling in my hair and squashed a bug; I thought I saw a shadow move near the deserted railroad station and reached over to see if Sam was still by my side. Trains continued to roar by all night, but toward dawn I did fall asleep. I dreamed crazy, mixed-up dreams. I dreamed I was sitting in the lecture hall listening to Professor Jansen. He was drawing something on the blackboard and talking about squares and holes, pegs and rounds. Did I hear him right? He had just said, "Now I will demonstrate how to fit a round square in a peg hole." when a strange little voice brought me back to the present. Yes, Ricky was a round square in a peg hole. I could see it would be an interesting two weeks. I was glad the camping part was only planned for one of those weeks.

When do we eat? I'm hungry."

The sun blinded me as I looked out of scratchy eyes at a grubby collection of tousle-haired boys with dirty, smudged faces and grimy hands. Ricky had both arms around Sam. Sam, at least had accepted him as one of the gang.

A washrag, towel and some ocean water made some improvement, but we would be lucky if we weren't picked up as vagrants. As I scrubbed Ricky's face he said, "That's fun to sleep on the beach. I wish I didn't ever have to wear pajamas; then I could dress real fast in the morning." I wondered what it would be like to be eight and alone with a strange family, and marveled at Ricky's adjustment and acceptance of this strange new way of life.

It was a beautiful day, and a good breakfast at a roadside cafe made yesterday's nightmare seem far away.

"Can we go to the San Diego Zoo today, Mom?" one of the boys asked.

"Not today, boys, we've got too much to do."

"I saw a bear once. Grandpa shot it." a small voice ventured.

The boys looked at me. I could hear their thoughts—"Aren't you going to scold him for telling lies, Mom?" I wondered how I was going to handle this. How could you explain psychological factors to three boys who had been brought up to regard truth as a basic law.

"Hey, boys," I said, "look at the ships coming into the harbor." It was a cowardly way out, but effective. I needed more time to figure this one out.

We were on the peninsula and saw a lighthouse ahead. A sign pointed to a free museum in the tower. Up the tower we went, gauking at all the encased treasures.

I saw a shark in Hawaii," the small voice again volunteered He experimented taking the spiraling steps two at a time. "Bet you guys never saw one." The boys, well ahead of us, didn't hear so I ignored it.

That afternoon we again searched for a camping spot. The camps close to San Diego were all closed to campers during June, July and August because of fire hazards. How foolish to spend the day sightseeing before finding a spot. Yesterday's ordeal suddenly loomed bright in my memory. Again it was almost dark with no place in sight. I was close to tears when we spotted a faded sign, "LAST RESORT—5 miles". Twenty-seven miles from San Diego, hot and dusty, the camp was perched on a cliff overlooking the ocean. A precarious path led almost straight down to the beach. It truly was the last resort, but right now it looked like paradise.

Pitching the tent was a real project. Lop-sided and sagging as it was, it was at least shelter. The Coleman lantern was more than we could cope with but a sympathetic tent-neighbor volunteered to light it. Camping had always seemed so simple when their father, was along. How could it be such a chore now?

While roasting marshmallows around the dying embers one night, I thought, "Maybe if he hears the story of the little boy who cried 'wolf' it will plant a seed in his mind." The boys looked a little bored with this old story, but probably figured Mom just didn't know how to tell stories like Dad.

Ricky listened to the story intently, but when the story was finished, crawled up in my lap and said, "I saw a wolf once." My heart sank. I held him tight and continued with another story. This one, I determined, would have no moral message.

It was soon time for bed. The fire was a small pile of glowing embers. Ricky had crawled into my heart as well as my arms and was sound asleep. It reminded me of a few years back when our boys were not so grown up. In spite of all the problems he caused, I was glad I had answered the phone that day.

The next few days went by on wings. Ricky seemed to have exchanged his tall tales for a siege of teasing. This seemed to be a more effective way of getting the attention he craved. The boys, of course, didn't appreciate the teasing but this was something they understood and new how to handle. Maybe the "Boy Who Cried Wolf" story had taken seed. My self-satisfaction turned to chagrin, however, while we watched a Navy helicopter traveling along the shoreline one morning.

"That's just like the helicopter that rescued me when I was on a surfboard in Hawaii." He took his turn with the binoculars. "Yep, just exactly like it." The boys just looked at him and shrugged their shoulders.

A day at the zoo seemed to spark even more imagination in this energetic little one. He flitted from one animal to the next and I could almost see his mind storing up new details for future use. We sent postcards to all our friends and relatives; Ricky wrote one to his folks. We returned to camp that night stuffed with cotton candy, popcorn and peanuts.

We were only about 20 miles from Tijuana, and one night we were talking about Mexico The boys knew quite a few Spanish words and they were wondering if we couldn't go to Tijuana. The idea intrigued me. None of us had ever been out of the States. We decided to leave early the next morning.

We were thrilled with the sights of this busy, colorful town. Burrows hauled brightly colored carts loaded with decorative jars, hand tooled leather objects, bongo drums and bright baubles of jewelry to catch one's eye. Store windows lured us with their splendid array of souvenirs.

Since our funds were limited, we enjoyed a delightful shopping tour with much dickering and little buying. Ricky held up a battery powered speedboat. "Look what I got for just $2.98. The woman wanted $5 for it, but I didn't have that much. Wasn't she nice to sell it cheaper?"

Larry tapped a set of bongo drums. "The man started out asking $7.00 but all I had was $3.00 so he decided to sell them for that." Bruce and Ron already had their hand-carved leather belts around their waists. "Look, Mom" they said "These only cost two dollars". I showed them my hand-carved leather purse that I tried not to buy, but couldn't pass up at $3.50.

"Gee, Mom, we sure got some good bargains, didn't we?" Bruce said as he dropped some change into his pocket.

We climbed into our VW bus and headed back to camp. As we approached the border station, the boys were unusually quiet. It had been a busy, exciting day for them.

The guard held up his hand for us to stop.

The first question he fired at me was. "Where were you born?" I answered, "Iowa".

"And the boys?" He peered into the car.

My heart froze! Where in the name of God had Ricky been born? I didn't have the slightest idea; it was far too late to ask him. How would I explain this brown-eyed little boy if I were questioned. I had no papers of any kind—what a fool I had been to go across the border.

With a prayer on my lips, I replied to the guard.

"They were born in Los Angeles".

"Oh, dear God, please keep Ricky quiet!" I expected to hear an impish voice say, "Oh, no I wasn't. I was born in China, or Hawaii or worse yet, Mexico."

Before I had time to take another breath, the next question was fired at me. "What did you purchase?"

"Just a few souvenirs," I said truthfully. The officer waved us on and I breathed again.

A few miles down the road, Ricky pulled something out of his shirt. "Look, what we bought in Mexico. Firecrackers! Boy was I scared when we stopped at the border. I was so scared I couldn't say anything."

So that was why they were all so quiet! I had seen the comic books they had and wondered if they realized they were printed in Spanish, but never dreamed they had purchased firecrackers.

I was too relieved to scold about the firecrackers and besides, being involved in this conspiracy seemed to have helped Ricky gain the attention he so desperately wanted.

The rest of our vacation would be spent at camp. No more sightseeing for this bunch! The boys swam in the surf and built sand castles which were swept away by the tides. One afternoon a storm gathered on the horizon and the boys came up from the beach covered with blotchy patches of tar. It was time to break camp and head for home.

Arriving home at 10:30 that night, we set up a de-tarring station on the front porch and methodically cleaned the boys, sending them in to take showers.

One by one they tumbled into nice clean beds in nice clean pajamas. I turned the tap on several times just to feel the luxury of instant hot water. I flicked a light switch on and off, just for the sheer joy of instant, quiet, odorless light.

The next morning I was greeted with a bear hug and the statement. "I've already had my breakfast, but I'll eat again with you." We enjoyed a leisurely breakfast while the sleepyheads snoozed on.

This was the pattern of life with our little guest the remainder of his stay with us. He loved getting his own breakfast, raiding the refrigerator during the day, teasing the boys and cuddling Sam. He reveled in just being a boy; something our boys had always accepted. To him it seemed more like a new adventure.

The phone interrupted our Saturday night dinner. It was his grandmother. I had almost forgotten he had a family; he seemed so much a part of ours now. A very pleasant voice on the phone shattered this illusion. "I so appreciate your taking care of Richard for us. We were frantic when we found we couldn't get away from Alaska sooner.

We would love to meet you, Mrs. Townsend. I wonder if it would be imposing to ask you to bring Richard home tomorrow instead of our driving down for him? Mr. Bascom and I are completely exhausted."

I assured her it would not be imposing. It would be a nice Sunday drive. "Wonderful. I'll have dinner for you. I'm just dying to meet you and the boys. We enjoyed Richard's postcard from the zoo, and he seemed so happy with you folks."

I told her approximately when we would arrive and she added, "Have the boys wear jeans. It's so dirty on the ranch." She gave further instructions for getting to their ranch and said, "Richard will tell you where to turn off the highway, and knows how to get to the house."

Sunday morning, after his usual second breakfast, Ricky insisted we fix a lunch to eat on the way. He seemed anxious to get home, but reluctant to leave his second family. It was going to be hard to say good-bye to this little one. I guess it was the strong mother instinct creeping out again.

The four boys in jeans, and I in mine, stopped at noon for our picnic lunch. Ricky tried to prolong it as much as possible, first by saying he wanted to stay with us. When I said that wasn't possible because his folks needed him, he suggested maybe we could all come live with them.

North of Santa Barbara, Ricky pointed to a side road and said that was where we turned off the highway. About a mile down the road, I pulled up at the very neat, well-kept, green ranch house. "Why are you stopping here?" Ricky asked. "This is the caretaker's house. That's our house up on the hill."

I was afraid to look. Old Yaller suddenly looked like a garish circus wagon; the boys in their jeans and I in mine looked like transient fruit pickers. We traveled up and up a winding road until we reached the pale green mansion, parked the car near the entrance and moments later were welcomed by his grandparents with great warmth.

As we climbed the stairs, his grandmother said, "You should have driven around to the front entrance." Now in the kitchen, Mrs. Bascom opened the oven door "See what is being prepared for you? Roast Chinese Duck!" I glanced at the gleaming kitchen, the uniformed cook and the golden brown birds in the oven and realized we had driven up to the servants' entrance.

As we were ushered through the deeply carpeted hall, I caught glimpses of long, luxurious sectionals, exquisite paintings, a grand piano, a large den with red leather chairs and a massive mahogany desk. I felt, rather than saw, the huge chandelier glittering above our heads. At the end of the hall, we entered a room decorated in bamboo. The view of the ocean from the large picture window and the sloping, green velvet lawn, enhanced the Hawaiian decor of the room. Richard prepared pineapple drinks for the boys while Mr. Bascom served cocktails. In the corner of the room stood a real surf board, and the boys sat quietly with wide eyes as Richard's grandmother told them about the time he was rescued by a Navy helicopter.

"Richard" was back home now, confident and sure of himself. This little round square had found his peg hole, and I resolved right then and there to give up amateur psychiatry.

Later, sitting in the beautiful patio, sipping champagne and eating roast Chinese Duck with Burgundy gravy, I was uncomfortably aware of my jeans which I could see through the glass table top. Sam shared a filet mignon with a dainty French poodle near the boys who were close by at another table.

Mr. Bascom told a few tales about hunting, fishing and the animals in Alaska.

Richard glowed with excitement. "Mother, after we eat can I take the boys out to see my Jeep?"

I glanced at the boys I had never seen them so quiet.

During our three or four years in Sunland/Tujunga, a lot happened. I went back to work. First as substitute help for the schools; then as secretary to Ross Welch, Director of Research at the electronics division of Elgin National Watch Company. Ash worked as a welder building the big electrical plant in North Hollywood.

We went through two major fires, but our house survived. During the first fire we had to evacuate. The boys lived through an explosion when Johnny, a neighbor boy mixed up some rocket fuel in their room. I survived a period of insect collecting—Tarantulas, scorpions, and trap-door spiders, and Ash got into Industrial Photography, taking construction pictures for the company Slim Robely worked for.

The Stephensons would move to San Jose to a new Lockheed job there. We would move to Seattle, with the prospect of another Alaska job building the refineries at Haines, Alaska. We planned to move to Haines for that job because it would mean permanent employment at the refineries, but due to some border dispute with Canada, the refineries were never built. Another detour.

SINK OR SELL-

There is a common understanding among small boat owners that you will continue to add accessories to your craft until it either sinks or you acquire a larger boat. The word "acquire" is used here purposely since I am convinced you don't purchase boats—they just happen to you.

It all started one balmy spring morning when I found myself staring at a freight bill in the amount of $39.27. After the initial shock had worn off, I made the startling discovery that my husband had "web" feet! It seems he had planned to surprise the boys and me with an eighteen foot fiberglass canoe from Herter's catalog. It would be hard to say who was the most surprised that day, the boys who had never seen a real canoe, myself who had never considered the possibility of owning one, or my husband with the freight bill which was exactly $34.74 more than he had anticipated. It seems the size of an object, as well as the weight, determines the shipping charge. Unfortunately, this little gem of a vessel was the same weight, but not the same size as a cannon ball.

It took a long time in the late 50s to work out a $34.74 kink in the budget, but the whole family was game. We started training immediately with a seafaring diet: lima beans, baked beans, pork and beans, chili beans, pinto beans (we even tried garbanzo beans), and ended up our two weeks with bullets and red lead (navy beans and catsup).

The canoe became quite a conversation piece in the neighborhood, which really isn't surprising when you consider that we were at that time living on top of a very dry mountain in southern California. The canoe became quite a conversation piece in our neighborhood, and our initial period of boat ownership was educational if nothing else. We learned how to compute freight rates, how to survive on a sailor's diet and that an eighteen foot fiberglass canoe sitting on a lawn leaves an eighteen foot canoe-shaped burn on the grass. We also learned that a canoe paddle cost $8.79.

Although it was never mentioned in our planning, I have the feeling that the canoe was a contributing factor in our move six months later. September found us settled in Seattle, within sight and sound of water.

SEATTLE

During the next two years, our bright yellow Volkswagen bus with overturned canoe on top became a familiar sight in the northwest. We learned to stretch our camping and boating season east of the Cascade mountains in early spring to avoid the rains; west of the mountains during the beautiful summer and back to the east part of the state in the fall.

We spent a lot of Wednesday afternoons (after work) on Lake Washington, and never missed the spectacular sight of the Wednesday sailboat races. In the shadow of all this splendor, the novelty of paddling a canoe palled, and the idea of adding a sail was born.

While the boys and their Dad sawed and sanded away in the basement, making a mast, lee boards and rudder, I struggled with twenty yards of bright yellow sailcloth Three weeks later the butterfly emerged from the cocoon as we unfurled the sails on Lake Washington. Along with her new costume she acquired a name, the Miss-Sailaneous.

The next opening day of the yachting season, she was rigged with a larger sail, a taller mast and a new two-horsepower motor. That year I had the dubious, but un-challenged distinction of being the only mother in Seattle who took a twenty mile canoe trip on Mother's Day. While other mothers were sleeping soundly, or being served breakfast in bed, I was travelling through the canal at the break of dawn and enjoying every minute of it.

The boys, in their teens now, is a phase I will skim over. I will let them tell stories about that period. I'm still hearing a few new ones even now. I remember many, many camping trips all over the state of Washington. The Alloways joined us by getting a Kombi too. Some of the trips I remember included kid friends of the families. One time on Camano Island, we pulled up at a State campgrounds and about six boys and the dog piled out. The campers next to us watched as we set up our tents. Then, when Owen and Marian and their gang drove up with their Kombi I heard the woman declare "Oh, my God, there's another one!" The Kombi's and Volkswagen buses were so new, people would stare at them and walk around peering in at the windows.

We went east of the mountains on opening day one time and Bruce caught a 23 inch trout. Ash also shot a rattlesnake that came into our camp. We took ferryboat trips to the Islands, camped on Hurricane Ridge in the Olympic National Forest and camped at a State Park on Olympic Peninsula where we picked oysters and a ranger taught us how to barbecue them. One time I looked on the map and saw so many lakes I bemoaned the fact that we'd never be able to see all of them.

At seventeen, Larry joined the Coast Guard and was first stationed at Coos Bay, Oregon. Later he was stationed for a year on Guard Island out of Ketchikan, Alaska and then Seattle where he took up mountain climbing with the Alloways.

PROMISES

When we left Tujunga, California to move to Seattle (1958), our little friend, Sandy Switzer, our adorable five-year old neighbor asked us to bring her one of the Washington Apples when we came back to California.

Two years later when we returned for a vacation, we remembered. Since we were not allowed to carry apples across the California border, we bought a sack of beautiful Washington apples at a store near Tujunga. On the way to their house, our three boys Larry, Bruce and Ron sat in the back seat and started the project of polishing them. When we presented them to Sandy, she turned to her Mother with a look of wonder on her face and said "See Mama, I told you they wouldn't forget!" What a reward! What a lesson we all learned. I wish I could say that all my promises were remembered, and kept, but that would be wishful thinking. For the times I have failed that vigil, I hope my family and dear friends will forgive me.

CHAPTER VII

THE 60's

After several years in Seattle, Ash was offered a job (through George Stephenson) as an Industrial Photographer for Lockheed in their special secret project conducted at Hiller Aircraft. Now known as the Corona project. Historically, the people who worked there called it the Skunk Works. Only a year or so ago was the project de-classified. Those who worked on that project can now reveal their involvement with the early spy satellites, U-2 planes and the Cuban Bay of Pigs incident. It was a scary time for Silicon Valley. Now, the books written about it call the people who worked at the Skunk Works "Pioneers". I always did think if we'd lived in the 1800s, we would have been on one of the first wagon trains. One of the best books on this is "Eye in the Sky" published by the Smithsonian Institution Press, 1998. The camera is in the Smithsonian Institute. The book is dedicated to the Corona Pioneers.

Ash had to be cleared by the Federal powers, so he went down in February and we were to follow as soon as Bruce graduated from, and Ron finished his sophomore year at Queen Anne High School. Larry was in the Coast Guard, stationed at Coos Bay, Oregon. I know this period will bring all kinds of memories of that era. When Bruce, Ron and I left Seattle in the Volkswagen Kombi, they were building the World's Fair Site at the bottom of Queene Anne hill. We stopped in Coos Bay to see Larry and the ship he was stationed on.

At the project, Ash was working long, long hours—one time he worked 26 hours in one day; came home for a few hours sleep and put in another shift of 26 hours. Yeah, I know there are only 24 hours in each day but this was what it was like.

SAN FRANCISCO AND THE HISTORIC SHIPS

One day, Bruce and I went to San Francisco to see what it was like. We both had cameras, and were going to test out different films on identical scenes. We were fascinated by all the sites, the cable cars and the hills that reminded us much of Seattle. We ended up on the waterfront and toured the Balclutha a beautiful, restored sailing ship. After taking pictures and climbing all over the ship, we went on down the waterway and saw another big sailing ship. Some sailors were carrying on cases of canned goods, and supplies. We decided to follow them and see if there was a charge or if we were even allowed to go on it.

Nobody said anything to us and we didn't see any ticket booth, so we proceeded to take pictures of men working in the rigging, and other interesting ship tackle and anchor lines. When we were through taking the pictures we wanted, we went back to the stairs and saw that we had come up one side of a stile. Down the other side was a policeman holding back the crowds waiting to get on. The line stretched so far we never saw the end of it. Later we would learn from the newspapers that the ship used in the movie "Mutiny on the Bounty" was in San Francisco for the day, and people would be allowed to go aboard.

In the fall, Bruce started college at San Jose State, and Ron started his last two years of high school. Larry was now stationed in Alaska. Later Ash and I would be involved with Friends of the Alma, one of the growing fleet of historic ships. During the time we were involved it was a State facility and later would become a National Park. Ron, Vicki, Conni and Kathryn would also be active in the historic ships and still are in touch with some they worked with. Ron still forwards pertinent and interesting information via e-mail. Hopefully they will preserve some of their interesting stories about the historic ships and San Francisco.

Ron's e-mail this morning (September 21, 1997) tells of the historic ferry boat Eureka as the new site for a television series "Nash Bridges" the police action drama starring Don Johnson.

This is just another tale of the interesting period of history we've lived through since 1919.

I went to work at Nordic Letter shop in downtown San Jose and learned more about offset printing and preparing the copy. This was just before the camera-ready copy era that led us into opening up our own print shop. Nordic Letter was in the daylight basement area of one of the old three story houses in downtown San Jose. The owners, Chris and Wally Wallberg, lived in an apartment above the shop and earlier had rented out rooms. The building was later torn down and a parking lot built there. The following is a story I wrote about their cat, as if told by the cat.

MUFFIN IS A NUFFIN

by
Muffin the Cat

I guess I'm pretty lucky to find this house? I think the whole picture will look better once I get over this illness. I felt fine until they took me to what they called "the Vet". Somehow when they say "Muffin is a Nuffin'" and laugh, I feel sort'a insulted, but the food is good and it's sure a lot warmer than out on the street.

In the daytime, we all go down into the basement and there are a lot of people coming in and out. It's a noisy place and smells funny—guess it's the ink and stuff they use to clean up the machine that makes all that noise. They call it a press. When it gets too bad I hide in the back where all the paper is stored. Of course I come out when it's lunch time and let Chris and Wally share my lunch. They eat more than I do so I let them put my little tidbits down here on the cement floor.

At night is the best time. They close and lock the front door and we go upstairs and have a real dinner with good smells floating through the apartment instead of that old ink! For the time being I see no reason not to let them keep me, but this Vet stuff has got to stop!

Well, I've been here for two years now and everything was going just great until today when one of the "customers" just came in and stayed. She uses Chris' machines, and they treat her like one of the family. I'll ignore her and see how long she's going to stay.

I'm still ignoring her and it's been almost another two years. She comes in every day, but does go home at night and everything is still the same upstairs. My food is always ready when I want it. Oh, well, what the heck!

This morning I came down the stairs and found my bed and litter box downstairs in the print shop. Wonder if I did something wrong? Well, everything seems as usual. People are going in and out, the girl is still here using the typewriter, typesetter and collator—boy I'm really getting smart living around this place. I did hear a new word today—Chris and Wally were talking to Ernestine (I really have known her name a long time, but don't let her know it). They said something about a "vacation". In the four years I've been here, I don't ever remember hearing that word, but it doesn't sound bad.

Now what's going on? Tonight we didn't go upstairs and Chris and Wally left to go out to dinner I think. They forgot to let me go up the stairs I checked and the door up there is shut. Oh, well, everything is here. I'll just eat and go to sleep. Everything will be OK in the morning.

Chris and Wally never came home??? But, the girl came as usual. I have been asking her all day what is going on, but she doesn't understand my language. Before she left at the regular time she left me a dish of food and water. Guess she's not too bad. Maybe I've been too harsh with her. Tomorrow I'll be a little more friendly.

The door is still locked upstairs. I wonder if they are ever coming back? There's the girl now, coming in the front door and she has a key! When she sits down at the typewriter I'll surprise her and jump up in her lap. Really she's pretty nice—pets me, feeds me and is even talking some to me. Maybe we could be friends.

Well, that does it. The upstairs door is still locked; no Chris and Wally. When Ernestine comes in today I'm going to get up in her lap and whisper in her ear "It's just you and me babe." Hey, I'm a hep cat!

WEDDINGS—We had reached the period in our lives when we would be empty nesters—First Ron and Vicki, then Larry and Susan, were married. Then, Bruce finished college and moved to his own apartment, working in the electronics industry that was rapidly developing what is now called Silicon Valley. Like my folks, we would become empty nesters, but still all our family was in San Jose and we were able to get together for family occasions and holiday festivities.

CORNED BEEF AND CABBAGE

Vicki calls this "Family Story #251".

Ron and Vicki had been married a month or so. Working around Ash's long hours on the secret project was still difficult, but we finally found a slot to invite them to dinner. A day or so before, Ron called and said "Mom, will you fix us some corned beef and cabbage?" I had planned a much more elaborate dinner and said "Well, that's not a very fancy dinner". He said, "I know, but that's what we want!" So, the menu was decided. At least I would have a special dessert.

They arrived a little early and we visited for a while and then I went to the kitchen. Vicki followed me and watched very closely while I prepared the corned beef and cabbage.

THE RECIPE

Scrub and cut into pieces some small potatoes (I like the red potatoes) . Put them in a large pot that has a lid.

Cut up some cabbage in chunks and add to the pot.

Open a can of Corned Beef and break apart over the top of the cabbage.

Add a cup of water and put the lid on.

Cook on medium heat until potatoes are done. Serve on a platter.

We would find out much later that she had been promising to cook him her special corned beef and cabbage. He kept telling her "Wait until you taste my Mom's".

CHAPTER VIII

THE 70's

When I think back on the 60s and 70s, my mind is a kaleidoscope of images and memories.

I'm not even going to try to keep it all in chronological order. All during the secret project and print shop ventures, there were marriages, boats, grandchildren, the Friends of the Alma at the San

Francisco maritime park and the Spinnaker Yacht Club . More boats would be acquired—the 27 ft. fixer-upper pictured above that we named "The T-Toter"; The 30 ft. Piver Trimaran Ash built during the madness that swept the country triggered by Art Piver and his adventures; boating on the Delta and San Francisco Bay; the Master Mariner's races on the Alma, Tropic Star and other boats, and printing a book about the Master Mariner's race of pictures taken from our last boat, the Silver Lining.

Our family and interests grew with marriages, grandchildren. We were so busy in the printing business that we had little time to spend with the four granddaughters who came along, but the times we did have together are very precious memories. We moved several times during this period and had a few more detours before we sold our last print shop to Jim Bush and retired to the Northwest.

When the Skunk Works closed, we started the print shop on Curtner Avenue, and George went on to the Glomar project. This was another super-secret project that has recently been de-classified to some extent.

The Glomar Explorer, built by Howard Hughes for the CIA was 619 feet long, and was designed to retrieve a Soviet submarine that sank in 1968 near Hawaii. The ship was built in Chester, Pennsylvania on the Delaware River and the crew was trained in Redwood City, California. The 36,000 ton ship housed a huge claw that could reach far down into the ocean and lift the submarine. It was a monumental task never before even dreamed of, but they did it in 1974.

Books have been written about this CIA project, and will be a part of the history of the 20th century we've lived through. One book about this in our library is titled "A Matter of Risk", published by Random House, New York in 1978.

GRANDKIDS—Conni, Cindy, Shawn and Kathryn—four cousins. Life's cycle was starting again. We didn't have a lot of spare time during the 70s when the granddaughters were arriving and growing up, but the few times we had them at the slumber parties, playing miniature golf, movies and the trip on the train to San Francisco for the day are very special memories. I remember the trip we took with Conni and Cindy on the boat. We were up in the Delta and they wanted to go see Angel Island. It was a 90 mile boat trip, and it was the usual "Are we there yet" type of trip. We finally reached San Pablo Bay when we heard a blood-curdling scream (I had heard that term before, but never realized what it meant). It was Cindy, and we panicked! When we finally got our breath back, and asked her why she had screamed. Her reply, with a smile on her face was "Oh, I was just out here where nobody could hear me, so I decided to see how loud I could yell".

When we got in sight of Angel Island, Conni piped up "Is that Hawaii"? I think by this time she thought they had been kidnapped. Anyway, we survived the weekend; got back to the Delta and on the way home, stopped at A&W for a hamburger. I think this was the highlight of the weekend.

One time when we had a slumber party at our apartment, the girls helped me learn how to work a new juicer I bought. We had a lot of fun in the small kitchen, putting different fruits and vegetables through the juicer. Shawn named her concoction "carapple juice" when she mixed apples and carrots.

Kathryn, you should have a lot of stories about this period of our family's life.

Ash worked many long hours on building the trimaran—another period of challenges. We led an active life in the printing businesses, yacht club, sailing, and boating on the delta. The following was an interesting trip.

ONE MINUTE OF MY LIFE

My first and only attempt at modern poetry

Our Trimaran on San Francisco Bay

Ash, the captain at the helm,
made a quick decision
to head for the lee shore
in water deep enough
for our sailboat, but too shallow
for the many big ships and tankers
plowing their way to Sacramento

As first mate, I was
stationed amidships on the port wing
to relay positions and potential hazards
to the captain.

With compass, depth sounder and charts,
we ventured through the thick fog,
charting our progress by identifying
the bells and buoy lights as we passed them
and listening for and locating
the mournful fog horns.

We almost collided with a small fishing boat,
but our system was working and
a mishap was avoided.

When by our calculations
we were approaching the Richmond Bridge,
the tension grew.
This would be the only part of our course
where we had to venture out
into the deep channel.

I was straining to see through the fog
which was thicker than before, when
I heard the deafening roar of
big engines, and
an unfamiliar, awful grating noise!

My heart stopped, my knees went weak
and I grabbed for the mast stay,
expecting the worst!

Just at the moment I expected to see
the bow of a big tanker
crash into and destroy our little vessel,
I realized the sound was coming
from directly over my head.

The roaring motors were
from big trucks;
the grating sounds were
their tires going over
the metal traction grids.

I regained my balance and
shouted over the din,
"All's clear!
We continued our course to
San Francisco Bay.

When we finally tied up
at Angel Island,
we collapsed and drank
a toast to our good fortune
and safe harbor.

The trimaran would be replaced with the 30 ft. diesel cruiser "Silver Lining" which would be with us through the end of the 20th century, and into the new millennium. We enjoyed many years of cruising in the Delta, and San Francisco Bay before we retired to the Northwest.

CHAPTER IX

THE 80's

We moved from San Jose, California to Anacortes in 1980 after selling our printing business. We had the Silver Lining shipped up to Oak Harbor on Whidbey Island. Walt and Fran Petersen rented us a small house on March Point a few miles east of Anacortes. There we met their rental managers Cecil and Joanne Cushman. They have become very special friends over the past twenty years. Five years later we moved into the town of Anacortes. At that time Anacortes had a population of 9,000 and had maintained that number for over 20 years. Now at the turn of the century, it is over 14,000, and still growing.

During the 80's our family grew with more weddings—Larry and Carol; Bruce and Shirley and their families. We would make new friends in Washington, and keep in touch with many of our old friends, cousins and families, especially after e-mail entered our lives.

Anacortes is located on an Island. I don't know how long we lived here before we discovered this. It is connected to the mainland by a bridge over the Swinomish Slough, and to Whidbey Island by Deception Pass Bridge. It is known as "The Gateway to the San Juan Islands" because on the west end of the island all the ferry boats leave for the Islands and Victoria, a very "British" city on Vancouver Island in Canada.

Our writing class was working on a book of short stories about our island, and Ron was investigating the new concepts of sophisticated P.C.s when I wrote the following short story.

WHERE IN THE U.S.A. IS FIDALGO ISLAND?

Ron could hardly wait to get home with his new computer game "Where in the U.S.A. is Fidalgo Island"? He had mastered all of the "Where in the World" games, but this was the latest and most difficult game yet—or so the advertisement said.

At his computer he fed in the symbols and punched all the keys according to the instructions. When the program came up on his monitor, he read:

ENTER YOUR NAME:

He entered his name and the game was on!

As he went through the first easy questions one by one, he came to one he couldn't answer.

WHO WAS LT. SALVADOR FIDALGO?

Well, that shouldn't be too difficult to find out—just switch to the Prodigy program and tap their six jillion byte encyclopedia.

LT. SALVADOR FIDALGO WAS A SPANISH EXPLORER

That's not much help—the Spaniards explored all of our continental coast areas—could be in the Florida Keyes, the Gulf Coast, California, or even in the Northwest. Fidalgo Island obviously was named for this explorer. Let's try "Fidalgo Island is in the Florida Keyes".

WRONG! TRY AGAIN, RON.

"Fidalgo Island is in the Channel Islands off the coast of California?"

WRONG AGAIN, BUT CLOSER. TRY AGAIN.
HINT: WHERE IS THE JEWEL COAST?

That's a real stumper. Well, back to Prodigy. "Where is the Jewel Coast?"

THE JEWEL COAST—A SHORT STRIP OF SCENIC COASTLINE BETWEEN THE CITIES OF ANACORTES AND BELLINGHAM, WASHINGTON.

Well, that settles it, it's got to be in the northwest. It can't be the Gulf Islands because that's Canada. Well, it must be in the San Juan Islands, but I don't remember any island in the San Juans called Fidalgo. My folks live in Anacortes, maybe I should just call them, but that would be sort of cheating wouldn't it? I've spent a lot of time in the islands, on my Dad's boat, on the ferries and on the whale watching boats out of Friday Harbor. If it's in the San Juans it must be an awfully small, unmarked island. Let's see, there are a lot of little islands out of Anacortes—the biggest in that area is Guemes. I remember the funny little ferryboat that travels across the channel. The islands where we go crabbing in my Dad's boat—if I remember right they are named Hat and Saddlebag Islands. The Jewel Coast??? I know there's an island off Bellingham called Lummi. Anacortes? I give up—guess I'll tap Prodigy again, and just for fun I'll feed in "Anacortes" and see what they come up with.

ANACORTES—A CITY 90 MILES NORTH OF SEATTLE, LOCATED ON FIDALGO ISLAND, GATEWAY TO THE SAN JUAN ISLANDS. They've got to be kidding! Anacortes isn't on an island. Or is it? Let's see, as Vicki put it, we drove north on Hiway 5 to the end of the world and turned left. If Anacortes is on an island, how did we get onto the island? No ferry boat, that's for sure. As tired as we were, we would have remembered that! I remember! We went over a bridge. We did see a sailboat and a railroad bridge was opening for it. There was a channel there! Guess we were too busy looking at the big Bingo Casino with all the RV's in the parking lot. It reminded us of Las Vegas. Well, guess I'll take a crack at breaking the code and winning the game.

"Fidalgo Island is an island north of Seattle, accessible by land. Point of departure to the San Juan Islands."

CONGRATULATIONS RON! YOU WIN!! YOUR PRIZE IS A COPY OF THE LATEST BEST SELLER BOOK TITLED "WHERE IN THE U.S.A. IS FIDALGO ISLAND", A COLLECTION OF RANDOM WRITINGS OF THE WEDNESDAY MORNING SENIOR WRITING CLASS ON FIDALGO ISLAND.

TO GET YOUR COPY, ENTER YOUR NAME AND ADDRESS PLUS CODE W-202 ON WEB SITE WWW.FIDALGO.COM. ALLOW SIX WEEKS FOR DELIVERY.

This was his reply to my story above:

Dear Mr. and Mrs. Townsend,

We regret to inform you that FIDALGO ISLAND, WASHINGTON does not exist, and you may be required to return to San Jose, California until this discrepancy can be rectified.

Your theories expressed in the game were interesting, but we have run into a minor technical difficulty. I sat down at my computer tonight, signed on to PRODIGY, and got into the Grolier's "American Academic Encyclopedia", and started looking for "Fidalgo" . . . the closest I came alphabetically was "fiddler crab". That would never do, so I looked up "San Juan Islands". Got a lot closer this time with "San Juan Puerto Rico", but still pretty far away geographically!

Going next for the bigger target, I asked for "Washington State" and got back an index indicating 42 pages of information. In that 42 pages, the closest I ever came to the San Juan Islands was "Puget Sound" and "Juan de Fuca straits". I printed out what information I got on those items, and a couple of more that got close to the subject in question, but nothing directly related to the San Juans or Fidalgo.

I decided to try the Old Fashioned Way, and look in the World Book Encyclopedia on the shelf above my right shoulder. It was printed in 1972, and some information is out of date, but I figured that the history of the 16th thru 19th centuries hasn't changed that much, so what the hey!

Uh oh!! Nothing in the "F book" between "fiction": and "fiddler crab"! OK, lets try "San Juan".

Hmmmmm. San Juan Puerto Rico again, San Juan Capistrano, San Juan Hill, Battle of. . . Ah ha! "SAN JUAN ISLAND NATIONAL HISTORICAL PARK. See National Park System (table)" and Ta Da . . . SAN JUAN ISLANDS are a group of over 170 islands bounded by Haro and Rosario straits. They lie between Washington and Vancouver Island, and belong to Washington. The islands, which cover 179 square miles (464 square kilometers) of land, have a population of 3,856. Lopez, Orcas and San Juan are the largest islands. The islands have less rainfall and more sunshine than

> the mainland. Most people work at farming, fishing or the tourist industry. Friday Harbor is the chief port. Spanish explorers named the islands. The United States acquired them from Britain in 1872." And, looking up the National Historical Park, the table shows that San Juan Island NHP is 1,752 acres, in Washington State, and it "Honors peaceful settlement of boundary dispute with Canada and Great Britain in 1872. ***Locally this is known as the "Pig War".*** So there you have it . . . Fidalgo, the explorer did not, and Fidalgo, the island does not, appear to exist!! Ron

BOATING IN THE 80's—We had many memorable trips with friends and family when they visited. Sometimes by ferry boat; in our boat; in charter boats in the San Juan Islands, and trips to Victoria and Vancouver, Canada. The last few years we were actively boating, we found a secret crabhole, and enjoyed many meals and boat trips a few miles out of Anacortes. Will leave those stories to those who enjoyed them with us.

SPRINGTIME AT CHATTERBOX FALLS

One of our trips in the Silver Lining up in the British Columbia waters above Vancouver.

The Fjords of Norway cannot possibly be as beautiful as Princess Louisa inlet in early spring. We carefully maneuvered the Silver Lining into the tricky Malibu rapids at slack tide. Entering the narrow passage lined with majestic peaks, we gazed in awe at the sheer cliffs that reached to the sky. This was April, and the peaks were still covered with snow. The crests of snow were iridescent and delicate with the bright sun shining through them. They looked as if ready to break off at any moment.

At the end of the passage we entered Chatterbox cove and shared the next few days with two seals and several seagulls. The rocky shore and still water presented an ever-changing display of totem images if you turned your head and looked at them sideways. The roar of the falls at the end of the passage gave a background of natural sound for the seagulls calling back and forth discussing our intrusion. The seals, very shy at first, grew bolder and even barked a few greetings in the early morn.

At the end of the very long dock, we discovered a guest log. It was hard to believe there were over two hundred visitors to this quiet spot in June. On shore there was a beautiful log shelter with a center fire pit. We could imagine the summer gatherings of high-spirited yachtsmen gathered around the fire. But, this was April. There was the essence of spring with the delicate wild flowers showing their color, and green ferns still curled, ready to spread their fans. The dormant trees were just beginning to show pale green leaves. This would be a most memorable spring, spent in nature's cathedral.

RE-ENACTMENT ERA

Information about the Lewis & Clark expedition and the origin of the Rendezvous that involved ancestors Patrick Gass and William Ashley, is included in my book "Other Centuries; Other Stories".

On our trip to Anacortes when we retired, we stopped at the Switzers in Klammath Falls, Oregon and Dick introduced Ash to a Black Powder Rendezvous. We would make several trips down to Klammath Falls for rendezvous and shoots, until one day I said "I think you should find a club closer to home—seems weird to drive 600 miles and back to shoot guns. So, he found first the Skagit Muzzle Loaders and later the Mount Baker Longrifles. Both clubs enjoy many activities, potlucks, shoots and tell tall tales at their rendezvous. We traveled to Camas Meadows, Grants Pass and other inter-club rendezvous during the time it was a very active movement. Now we've given up tenting and keep a small trailer at the beautiful meadow where the Mount Baker Longrifles hold their shoots and rendezvous in the Mount Baker foothills.

As we near the end of the 20th century, it is interesting to observe the many clubs and organizations that re-enact our history. Conni and Brian belong to the SCA (Society of Creative Anacronysms). They re-enact the 1600's with sword fights, colorful costumes and primitive camps. There are also Renaissance Fairs of that period. Our blackpowder club re-enacts the mountain man period of our history in the early 1800's. In the South they re-enact Civil War times, and on the east coast the Revolutionary War period. These clubs rendezvous all over the United States and some all over the world. Will future generations re-enact the 20th century? Only time will tell.

BLACK POWDER RENDEZVOUS

We attended our first big rendezvous in Camas Meadows, near Leavenworth, Washington. Standing on a nearby hill where a few horses were tethered, I counted 127 tipis. I also saw the tents on Trader's Row. People were coming in and out of the tipis; children, dressed in primitive clothes, were playing and the sound of guns in the far field made me feel that I really was living in those times. The modern "Tin Tipis" (RV's) were hidden in an area back of Traders Row.

Now I walked down the hill, past the Tipis and wandered through Trader's Row. Tents were set up to sell enamel ware, cast iron cooking pots, prairie dresses, buckskins, Indian moccasins, and all kinds of primitive foods. A blacksmith was busy making tools and shodding a horse. Antique blackpowder guns were on display for sale and you could hear the booms and see the white smoke of the blackpowder gun battles being re-enacted.

Later, around a big campfire, the men were telling their tall tales, the women were preparing the beans in a big cast iron pot and the children were running around the campfire area playing tag, hide-and-seek and Indian games. A pig was roasting above an open fire pit and it was a warm, dry night with a clear, star-studded sky. Never in the cities did you see a sky like that.

Later in the evening, sitting around the campfire we looked up in the sky. There was a feeling of belonging; not just to that group, but to the heavens above and the ancestors who pioneered the settlement of the west. William Ashley is credited with starting the idea of the rendezvous so popular during the fur trading era.

"Oh, look" one of the children shouted. "There's a satellite!" We all looked up and spotted the "moving star" slowly traveling across the star-studded sky. In the next hour we would spot seven more satellites, and the spell was broken. We were back in our modern world, dressed in costumes.

RENDEZVOUS APPLE PIE

by Ash Townsend

For the uninitiated, it must first be explained that there are two (2) definitely different kinds of Apple Pie. First, and probably best known, there is Mom's and Grandma's Apple Pie. There's no point in arguing whose Mom or Grandma makes the best apple pie—by America's tradition, everybody's Mom or Grandma makes the best apple pie in the world!

Then there's the other kind of Apple Pie that not everybody's Mom or Grandma can or will make. I was introduced to it at the Jed Smith Black Powder Rendezvous at Grants Pass, Oregon in 1987.

I had just finished pitching my tent and storing my gear. When I stood up and lighted my pipe an old friend I'd never met before walked up and said "Howdy". Well, I Howdied him back and he introduced himself as "Lonesome Elk"—Stravinsky I think.

After we'd discussed the weather and the crowd, he said "Would you like some Apple Pie"? I looked at my watch and said it was gettin' on towards supper time, but "Yeah—a small piece would taste real good." He returned in a couple of minutes with a Cow Horn hangin' 'round his neck and a stoneware jug in his hand. When he blew on that horn, it sounded like the plumb lonesomest Elk in the whole world!

Then he pulled the corn cob out of the jug and said "Have some apple pie". I learned later that I committed a faux pas—I sniffed the jug! You just don't do that to a jug passed in friendship. Besides you might not want to know what's in it and it's considered tacky to gag before drinking.

No such problem with this jug though, I could hardly believe what my nose was tellin' me—APPLE PIE !!! So, I took a sip (another "No, No"), and it was still APPLE PIE as good as Mom ever made—brown sugar, cinnamon, cloves, everything—so I took a gulp and Lonesome Elk reached for the jug, and said "You're welcome to all you can handle Pilgrim, but that's got a 180 proof rum base and two gulps is about all the average man can handle. Three minutes later I believed him!

A little later, a young feller makin' the rounds stopped by the camp and was offered a shot of Apple Pie. He'd already made a couple too many stops, and when he tipped the jug up, he tipped her a little too fur, stepped back to catch his balance and there were three of us at a dead run trying to catch that jug.

Losing a jug of Apple Pie could spoil the whole evening. Besides, it's a good idea to save a little of it to help start the fire in the morning.

RENDEZVOUS APPLE PIE RECIPE

Ingredients:
2 quarts water
1/2 cup honey
1/4 cup light brown sugar
1 tsp. apple pie spice
3 cinnamon sticks
2 cans (12 oz.) frozen apple juice undiluted
2 cups 100-proof light rum
(180 proof can be used, but watch out!)

Add cinnamon sticks to 1 quart of the water
simmer in a stainless steel or enamel pan for 30 minutes
Leave cinnamon sticks in.
Add honey, sugar, and apple pie spice.
Continue to stir and simmer until dissolved and blended
Remove from heat.
Add the fozen apple juice, the additional quart of water, and
the rum, stirring until completely dissolved and blended.

Bottle and keep in refrigerator for one week.
It can be taste-tested at any time.
They say it improves with age,
but I haven't heard of any lasting long enough to prove it.

TALL TALES A PASTIME OF RENDEZVOUS

We sent the family a picture of the two of us in front of a covered wagon. I had on a complete primitive costume, prairie dress, bonnet and moccasins. Ash was wearing a complete buckskin outfit with a black powder rifle by his side. We got a letter back from Vicki saying she didn't know the digital Indians of California had traveled that far north. She had spotted my wrist watch. The following is a tall tale published in the June/July 1984 issue of Black Powder Times and sent to her as an explanation.

TALL TALES

or

How to explain that Blasted Digital Watch that Shows Up in Your Favorite Buckskin Picture!

By Erni Townsend

I'm glad you noticed the digital watch on the buckskinner's arm. No, it wasn't a trader's item from the Digital Indians in California. Actually, it is a replica of a time piece invented by one of the Northwest Indian chiefs. His name was Chief Hoh-Kee (in English, pronounced Hokey). The Indians in this great Northwest, where the sun shines no more forever, were for the most part, good natured, easy going and happy since there was an abundance of clams, oysters and other seafood. There actually was a lot of deer and other animals to hunt, but they did very little of that since the sea provided plenty and the land provided vegetation in great abundance, with blackberries and huckleberries for special treats. Also, because of the abundance of food, time was unimportant to them, so they first treated Chief Hoh-Kee's new invention as a joke and every time he showed it to the tribe there were great peals of laughter. To make it more attractive, and to help the tribe accept his great invention, he designed a wristband, decorated it and tried to get the tribe to see what a great invention it was. The tribe still laughed at him and the children giggled and imitated him by looking at their wrists every few minutes.

Chief Hoh-Kee was really a genius, so instead of trying to convince the tribe that he could tell time, even without the sun or a sundial like they had all seen on the tall ships that sometimes came to their shores, he studied the tides very carefully. He finally discovered the pattern of the tides and since their very livelihood depended on the tides for picking oysters, digging clams and diving for crab and shrimp, he started predicting ahead of time when the tides would be low according to his watch. His predictions were so accurate that the tribe really became alarmed and were all convinced he was a witch. They started ostracizing him from their activities and the tribal council was called to banish him from the tribe.

Heartbroken and discouraged, he disappeared into the forest and the story of the Witch Chief who could tell time without the sun was handed down from generation to generation and to this day everyone knows what a Witch Watch looks like.

TRIPS AND CRUISES—I never expected to travel in foreign countries. In the 70's Ash and I did take a ferryboat trip to Alaska. That was the farthest I'd ever been away from the Continental United States. Aunt Esther, John Ashley's wife, called one day and asked that Ash sit down. She said she had tickets for us to take a cruise to the Caribbean, and all we had to do was to bring pocket money to buy souvenirs. What a delightful experience that was. If I live long enough I could write another book about that and the other four trips with her and her son, Rex Cherryman.

We would enjoy our time with them as we traveled up the Rhone River in France, to Lyon then on to Paris on a fast train; another trip down the Rhone River and on to Switzerland, and the last trip to Hawaii. On all the trips we were booked on tour ships—always had a room that traveled with us. In Hawaii, we visited three or four of the Islands.

While in Avignon, France, Ash had some congestion, and I walked from the ship up to the town and found a pharmacy. Their stores don't have shopping baskets, so you go to the pharmacist and ask for what you want. I asked the man for "Kleenex" and he looked blank; then I remember the French word for paper was "tissue", so I asked for that. Still no response. So, I did the next thing I thought might get the point across and went through the actions of blowing my nose. He looked bright and went back to a shelf and brought back some nose drops. I shook my head and went through the whole act again of blowing my nose. He turned around and went back to another shelf and came back with the package that said "Kleenex Tissue". I was flustered, but recalled the cruise director's instructions to always remember to say "Merci beau coup". His reply in perfect English was "You're Welcome". I did manage to get out of the store before I burst out laughing. I had been had! We found the French people very nice and helpful in our attempt to communicate without knowing their language.

One summer, Aunt Esther and Rex came to visit us. What a picture to see her on our boat when we went to catch crabs, and another day when we went to Orcas Island. She thought the champagne brunch at the Rosario Inn was really world class. She would live to be 96 years old, and realize her dream of flying on a Concord. We also spent some time with them in Virginia Beach when she called and wanted us to come back and pick up Dreamboat, her old Cadilac that had been so much a part of her life. On our way home we stopped to do some sight-seeing at Jamestown, Williamsburg and Montecello, the Thomas Jefferson's estate.

POLTERGEISTS

Conni's poem with a twist
If you don't believe in Poltergeists,
And don't really think they're true.
The Poltergeists you discredit
May choose to visit you!

The American Heritage Dictionary describes a Poltergeist as a ghost that makes noises and rappings. But to those they visit, they are much, much more. To keep us from finding out about them, in some dictionaries they erase any listing of the word "poltergeist".

Most are pranksters. They hide things you just put down, move things to places you know you never left them They seem to become more active the older you get and you tend to blame it on your memory. But how do you explain an electric razor that turns itself on inside the medicine chest? Or, a hearing aid that shows up in the middle of the night in your hand when you and everyone else have been looking for it for two days?

It is common knowledge they are more active after little children have been visiting. Maybe they are ghost children and like teasing their elders? They seem to like homes where children are welcomed and loved. Sometimes, to get your attention, they will push a glass of water off the table and drop things out of the cupboard or refrigerator.

And, oh do they have fun with the computers and new electronic equipment. You set your VCR to tape a program and they tape something else. They ring your fax and it says it's receiving but nothing comes out. They hide icons on your computer, or really have fun re-arranging them. They delete programs and sometimes deny access.

Whether you believe in the little devils or not, it's fun to have someone to blame for all the unexplainable things that happen in your golden years.

A MEMORABLE CANOE TRIP

(August 1986)

Cecil and Joanne Cushman talked us into joining them on a canoe trip. We were able to schedule it so we would be back in time for my Mother's first summer visit. She had recently moved from her home to my brother's place in Glendale, California. To give them some freedom to travel, we had arranged to have her stay with us during the summer months. We now lived in Anacortes in a larger home. She was 94 years old and we looked forward to her being with us with her bright sense of humor.

We had CB's in our vehicles. Ash and Cecil kept up a lively conversation all the way. Cecil has lived and hiked and camped in so many places in the Northwest that he is a very knowledgeable and entertaining tour guide.

Our destination was Bowren Lake Provincial Park. Bowren Lake was one of a chain of lakes surrounding a mountain, located about 500 miles north of Vancouver, British Columbia in Canada. At the lodge, we packed and launched the canoes. The first night we set up camp on shore at a campground. It as the first time I'd ever seen or heard of a bear-proof ladder storage structure. The park is kept primitive except for the few cabins, built during pioneer days before it became a park. They are available on first come basis.

We confined our canoe trip to Bowren Lake, but Cecil and Joanne had in the past taken the full circuit with many portages. The wild animals we saw on shore, elk, deer, raccoons, the bear-proof storage areas in the camp spots, bear tracks and beaver dams gave you the feeling you'd stepped back in time.

We found a vacant cabin the second day out in the canoes; explored the area and settled down in what graffiti described as "The Mouse House". The cabin had a picnic table, benches and a stove. We stretched out on the floor in our sleeping bags after a good camp dinner, including some huckleberries and fresh water clams Cecil and Joanne had found near the shore in shallow water. The next morning they decided to go on to the falls. We opted to stay put, not being sure we could handle portaging.

Others who had camped nearby also went on and we were alone. There was an eerie feeling of silence. We could hear the patter of the tiny squirrel's feet as they scampered around near the cabin. Even the shush of the birds' wings above us was audible. After years of living in cities and our present home being in the flight pattern of Whidbey Island Naval Air base, the silence was almost unearthly.

We walked down to the beaver pond, observed many wild animal tracks, picked some more wild huckleberries, and just sat in front of the cabin enjoying the small animals, birds and the eerie silence. Later, we went down to the beach, dabbled our feet in the water and sat there until dark. After dinner, we climbed into our sleeping bags stretched out on the floor. It was very quiet, but we did hear the sounds of mice cavorting around the cabin.

Sometime during that night I felt myself being carried up into the dark. As "we" passed through the roof, I glanced back and saw I was still asleep in the sleeping bag. I understood without words I was being taken somewhere to be shown something; sort of how I felt during my childhood when my brothers let me go with them to the forbidden pond to fish, pick wild berries, catch crawdads or tease the snapping turtles.

There was no sense of "time" but we did enter a very bright blue/white area, and there were many other "beings" there. It seemed like a spiritual, family reunion of loved ones, although none were visible. Then, I did see my father. He was young, dressed up, tall and thin. Not in the aged body I had last seen him. He did not see me. He was pacing back and forth outside an area that was hidden from view by a big white cloud that was so bright it was hard to understand why it didn't hurt my eyes. I knew without words that I was not allowed to see or enter that area. I understood Dad was waiting for my Mother and couldn't understand why she wasn't there with him. He wanted to show her this wonderful, beautiful place. During the whole experience, my father was the only person I actually saw visually.

Then, I was alone with an indescribable sense of being able to look down on the world. During the whole experience there was a sense of peace, love and joy, and a powerful feeling of being at the center of knowledge. No more struggle to understand complex matters. The feelings are hard to describe, but they are as clear today as they were during my venture into the other world. I do not remember being returned to my body, but was rather surprised to wake up the next morning, still in my sleeping bag. I had never heard or read of anyone having such an experience. I was anxious and concerned about my Mother, but didn't know how to tell Ash or our friends about the really strange "dream". We would be heading back home the next day where I could use a phone and call Don and Rowena.

The next morning, Cecil and Joanne challenged us to a 30 mile race back to the lodge in the canoes, We did it in one day instead of two. This gave us another day to explore Barkersville, a completely restored gold mine town, Docents dressed in 18th century outfits operated "Wake Up Jake" restaurant, a Newspaper and Print Shop, Church, Courthouse with mock trials and a hanging judge, and even a "House of Ill Repute" with mannequins. We met Cecil's cousin who drove a team and wagon up the street, dressed for the part. Then we went to the theater and were told two of the young actors had died going over the falls Cecil and Joanne had gone to see. They were sad, but said the boys would insist the "Show Must Go On".

The theater with the usual corny vaudeville acts, reminded us of the Blackguard theater in Hollywood, but the audience was rather sedate, instead of raucous as they were in California. The pianist kept the show going by prompting and playing lively music. On the stage, two men were talking as if they were living in the 1800's. One played the dummy and was constantly being prompted by the pianist. This went on for a while and the straight man said "I hear you have some camels here". The dummy said, "Oh, yeah, I had lunch with one the other day". The other guy looked at him funny and the pianist was trying to prompt him when the dummy said "Let's see, where was I"?

Ash couldn't pass up this opening and yelled out "You were out to lunch!" The pianist and the two guys on the stage cracked up and were laughing so hard it almost stopped the show. After the show when the players all gathered out in front of the theater to talk to the audience and sign autographs, the pianist came over and talked to us, and laughed about Ash's remark. Ash told her his aunt Esther, married to Rex Cherryman a well-known actor in the silent movie days, often used that term when referring to someone who wasn't quite all there. She said it was still a theater quip.

As during our trip up to Bowren Lake, Cecil and Ash kept up a lively conversation with our CB radios as we traveled a different route home. This trip will always be a special highlight in our retirement years.

Back home, a few days later, I went first to the phone and called my brother Don. He told me Mom had suffered a major stroke and had been in a coma for a number of days, but was recovering. I immediately made arrangements to fly down to Glendale to care for her while they went on their planned trip. Mom did recover from the coma, but would require extensive care at home, so plans for her staying with us during the summers would not work out. We would be spending time there instead.

About a year later, while at a family reunion in Seattle, I picked up a well-worn paperback on the table where the young mothers of the family were gathered. Robin, a niece said "Take it home if you like." All through the book there were many hand-written notes. I thought it was one she had used in a class. The book was Dr. Raymond Moody's "Life after Life". I discovered to my amazement that many people actually had surprisingly similar experiences. The big difference was the people he interviewed were in Near Death Experiences (NDE); not involved with a NDE that happened to another person 2,000 miles away. Then I recalled my Grandmother's story about her vision of Grandpa on the railroad tracks. Now in our satellite world, it doesn't seem too impossible that one might under certain conditions and locations "tune in" on something happening elsewhere.

I would not find out until years later that this very special book I still have was just one Robin had picked up at a yard sale. I still have only related this experience to a few people. I really don't have the words to express what happened. My coming into the possession of that book and other incidents that have happened since convince me that we aren't supposed to understand what the universe is all about, or how our lives are influenced by certain circumstances. In the 1980's, Pollster George Gallup, Jr., found that 8,000,000 adults in the United States have had Near Death, and Out of the Body Experiences. I have seen references to experiences like mine, but very little information about incidents involving another person's near death events. I have only met one person with a similar experience. It is something people feel reluctant to discuss in general conversations. There are groups listed on Internet that are researching and studying NDE's and some support groups forming where people can meet others with similar experiences.

Each person's experience is different, but there is a common thread of feelings expressed in personal terms. Because the event is so unusual, I have found it's hard to describe. It was a relief to me to find from Dr. Moody's books that others have had similar experiences.

While in Glendale, taking care of my Mother, I started studying Orthomolecular Nutrition (the therapeutic use of diet and supplements). I'd been researching and practicing natural healing for many years, but had no formal education in the subject. The American Nutrition Consultants Association was a school, approved by the State of California Board of Education. I received my degree in 1987. It has been the foundation for my continuing research and serious writing.

Our lives changed after that experience and we took on some serious commitments—mine in writing and Ash in starting and completing the Senior Center building project, as well as other important volunteer work. He was elected President of the Senior Advisory board when the seniors met in the basement of City Hall. In his nine years as president he was active in the fund-raising, architectural decisions, satisfying the requirements of the City, Parks Department, County, State, Federal government and the Presbyterian Church. The beautiful Community Center also houses a Head Start group, and is open to community events during the times the

Seniors are not using it. At the turn of the century, the mortgage has been paid off by the citizens of Anacortes (not tax dollars). He is still involved in the Center, several community boards and the Kiwanis.

I have become more and more involved in writing. This will be my third book to be published. If I live long enough, I have two or three others planned. Did all I have learned about natural healing help us reach these goals? Did the "out of body" experience have anything to do with the changes in our lives? Who knows. I'm sure I don't.

In 1988, on New Year's Day we had our first real emergency—911 was called and Ash was saved from his first aneurysm by the hospital, doctors and nurses, with a helicopter ambulance ride to Virginia Mason in Seattle. Then on New Year's weekend in 1990 a hurricane velocity wind hit this area, blowing down many big trees and destroying our boat house along with eight others. Our lives changed. We took on some major, important projects.

CHAPTER X

THE 90's

The 90s have been a busy, productive period in our lives and still are as we enter the new millennium. This is one of my articles published locally.

SOMETHING I'D LIKE TO CHANGE

Ernestine Townsend, R.N.C.

We are embroiled in a very confusing period of hype and hope concerning our health care as we know it today. Much of the information about diet is to promote products.

Our government, in the late 70s, decided we should switch to a high carbohydrate/low fat diet. This theory was based on many studies of primitive societies in Africa, India and Third World countries. It was noted these primitives did not have our modern diseases such as cancer and heart disease, strokes, Alzheimer's and obesity. I did not see any information about what they did die of or how their life span compared to ours. You can bet your bottom dollar their carbohydrates did not come in a box with sugar coating.

The government guidelines did include complex carbohydrates, but that seems to have been buried under a heap of advertising. The cereal industry has exploded, as have the prices. Big boxes of corn flakes that used to be less than a dollar are now closer to four dollars. Try finding a box of cereal that is not refined with no sugar or chemical additives. Oatmeal is about the only one you'll find on the shelves, and there are many flavored varieties of oatmeal that do use food additives.

We are told fat is not good for us, but most of the oils, margarine, and homogenized oil have been chemically extracted. The chemicals used can hide the rancid taste and odor. Rancid oil destroys needed nutrients, and oil products that do not spoil cannot digest. So, what happens to the undigested rancid oils?

We are told we all eat too much protein. Nothing is said about the quality of the protein. Meat products from animals fed steroids, antibiotics and hormones to promote growth are what we buy at the market. We probably do eat too much of this protein, but what choice do we have?

How would I change all this?

Remove the Food division from the Food and Drug Administration (FDA). Have a Drug Administration to control drugs and a Food Administration to regulate the food industry.

Each division would have strict conflict of interest restrictions on all administrative personnel. We do need regulations, but Food and Drugs are two entirely different entities. Unfortunately, we have reached a point where the government needs to be regulated and removed from the influence of big business lobbies.

Now I'll get off my soap box and get on with some humor. Laughter really has been proven to be a healing factor. So, here are a few of my contributions. Enjoy and let them trigger other stories and jokes.

THE HUMOROUS SIDE OF DIETING

Erma Bombeck style

The other day I told Harry I thought we should give up potatoes because I read they are part of the nightshade family. Well, he blew his stack and said if he had to give up potatoes, just go ahead and make his headstone right now!

Well, that settled that argument, so when I went to the store I decided if we couldn't give up potatoes I'd start following the government's new guidelines, read labels and try to improve our diet.

In the cereal department I picked up a package of Harry's favorite breakfast cereal—corn flakes (he always calls them Post Toasties). Then, I started to read the label. Corn (I would hope so), sugar, salt, malt flavoring, corn syrup. Well that didn't sound too bad so into my cart it went. At least the corn was the main ingredient. There are some government regulations that require the label to list the ingredients in the order of their percentage of the whole product.

It was more fun getting stuff like soap, toilet paper, paper napkins and paper towels where I didn't have to read the labels.

Mabel said a cheese cake mix you didn't have to bake was really good so I decided to have that as a real treat after dinner. When I read the label on that I almost had a heart attack! This is actually what it said:

INGREDIENTS: Sugar, Baker's cheese (skim milk, lactic acid, cultures) hydrogenated vegetable oils (coconut, palm kernel and soybean), corn syrup solids, tapioca starch modified, sodium phosphates (for thickening), sodium caseinate (from milk). ***Did you know milk has sodium*** caseinate in it? To go on, propylene glycol monostearate for blending, dipotassium phosphate, salt, mono-and diglycerides for blending; BHA (preservative), yellow 5, artificial flavor, natural flavor, yellow 6, beta carotene (for color). (At least I've heard beta carotene is good for you), citric acid (preservative). ***That was just the filling***!

Now we get to the crust: enriched wheat flour (flour, niacin, reduced iron, thiamin mononitrate, riboflavin, graham flour, sugar, partially hydrogenated vegetable oils (soybean and/or cottonseed, and/or canola), molasses, high fructose corn syrup, salt, baking soda, BHA, TBHQ and citric acid (preservatives).

Well, I couldn't wait to get that little bomb back on the shelf. After reading more labels (none as scary as that one) I decided to go to the bakery and get some bread. A woman was standing in front of shelf after shelf of different breads. With a resigned sigh, she said "Wasn't it wonderful when you just had to decide on white or brown?" I didn't bother reading labels; how do you make a sandwich without bread? I hurriedly picked up a loaf of sourdough (Harry's favorite).

Now to the meat department. What a relief! Nothing was labeled—it was just meat! The lunch meats, hot dogs and stuff like that had more scary labels so I'd just stop at the Deli and get some thin sliced ham or beef for sandwiches.

By this time, I realized that most of the food stuff in the perimeter of the store was not labeled; the processed foods and scary labels were in the center of the store. So, walking around the perimeter of the store, I finished my shopping. While standing in line at the checkout stand, a man from the next line came over, pointed at the box of corn flakes and said "Hey, don't you know you have to eat seven bowls of that stuff to get as much food value as the stuff I have in my basket? After a good laugh, we discussed the new government food label requirements. He said he never read labels—didn't really want to know what kind of junk he was putting in his stomach.

For supper, we had steak, potatoes and a vegetable salad with basil and rosemary herbs, vinegar and extra virgin olive oil. For dessert a slice of watermelon. Harry was delighted and the next morning while I was fixing his favorite breakfast of bacon and eggs he propped the following poem in front of my plate.

DIETER'S LAMENT

By
Ash Townsend

Here lies a man, let's call him Bud
Who died for want of an Idaho spud.

He always claimed his hair was wavy,
Because of his love of biscuits and gravy.

Here in his grave he'll always lie,
Because they refused him his apple pie.
The doctors told him he'd end up a leper
If he didn't give up his Salt and Pepper.

He said he'd go jump in the lake
If his wife didn't bake him a chocolate cake.

He never lacked for pleasure and cheer,
As long as he had his bottle of beer.

His biggest love was bacon and eggs,
And drinking his coffee down to the dregs.

His cigarettes and pipe he always did cherish,
Though doctors said he surely would perish.

Now old Bud lies in his grave secure.
The worms won't touch him that's for sure!

IS CHOCOLATE ADDICTIVE?

Everyone knows how serious I am about nutrition, but there is another factor that helps put it all together. Norman Cousins in his book "Anatomy of an Illness" told how, with the help of his doctor, he took massive doses of vitamin C, watched funny movies and laughed himself well.

An article in the journal "Nature", reported scientists have discovered a substance in chocolate that might mimic marijuana. Other scientists researching the subject agreed with the conclusion but found that a 130 pound person would have to eat 25 pounds of chocolate to get any euphoric effect. ***Most chocaholics say what's wrong with 25 pounds of chocolate?***

Some doctors and nutritionists have long puzzled over the fact that many individuals, particularly women, crave chocolate. Theories have ranged from a craving for the sugar contained in most chocolate products, to the fact that chocolate contains magnesium a nutrient particularly needed by women. Most just state they know it is addictive to some people but don't know why.

All of the above information has been reported in the regular news media recently. The following are my observations and comments supporting my belief that laughter really is the best medicine.

It is projected that a new, extensive study should be conducted to discover how many women keep a bag of chocolate chips handy, using a small handful for a quick fix whenever they get the craving. Does this mean that government regulations might ban chocolate? Might our first woman president admit that she did indulge in chocolate, but never "swallowed" it? Has this fear already started? On Wednesday, July 9, 1998 our local Police Blotter reported the theft of seven compact discs and a king size Milky Way bar from an unlocked car.

If the FDA bans it as being scientifically untested, will it become a black market item? Will there be M&M munch houses in old abandoned buildings? Will Hershey bars be sold on street corners and our jails glutted with chocolate pushers? Will our children be searched for chocolate candy bars before entering school grounds? Or, will new chocolate products be developed with this substance removed? We already have sugar-free products, decaffeinated coffee, lite beer, and filtered cigarettes to reduce other mood-altering substances.

Some health professionals consider chocolate one of the major food groups, and recommend the colorful round tablets with the little "m" printed on them. The "m" stands for "medicine" to treat CDS (Chocolate Deficiency Syndrome).

Unless you have been tested and found allergic, or have dietary restrictions that ban chocolate, the next time you get the craving, indulge. The magnesium will do you good. Like Mothers and warm cookies, it will make you feel better, and I'm sure you will be satisfied before you get a drug "high" or get sick.

HEALTH IN HEAVEN

John and Helen were in their eighties. Helen was a nutritionist, and did everything she could to keep them healthy, but they were killed in an automobile accident. When they arrived at the Pearly Gates, St. Peter welcomed them in and took them on a tour of Heaven.

He showed them to their mansion with modern kitchen, master suite and a Jacuzzi. From the deck they looked out upon the golf course. St. Peter told them each day it was changed to be like one of the most famous golf courses. John said, "How much does it cost?"

"Nothing", said St. Peter. "It's free, and you get your choice of clubs"

"What about my arthritis?"

"This is Heaven", said St. Peter. "There is no pain in Heaven".

The next stop was a banquet table with every kind of exotic, rich food imaginable.

"How much does it cost?" asked John.

St. Peter replied with some exasperation, "Nothing—this is Heaven. Everything is free"!

"Well, what about all that cholesterol, and fat?"

St. Peter said sharply, "You can eat all you want, and it won't hurt you!" This is Heaven".

At this, John became enraged. He threw his hat down, cursing and stomping his feet! When they finally got him calmed down, St. Peter said "What's wrong, John?" John shouted at Helen "If it hadn't been for your blasted bran muffins and broccoli, I'd a been here ten years ago!"

In our writing class, our assignment was to write a poem. We had been discussing modern poetry versus rhyming poetry with rhythm. My friend, Carmelita and I consider modern poetry just prose written in short lines. Anyway, just for the record, I did my homework.

RHYME

I watched a dumb program on TV
It was all about modern poetry.

In all their ravings about crime,
I never heard one word with rhyme.

When the program was over,
I called my dog Rover,
And went for a walk in the clover.

MODERN POETRY

I wish they'd find some new name
for what they now call poetry.

Remember the hours and days
Spent in our early years
Trying to understand rhyme and rhythm,
The essentials for creating poetry?

If we'd written like they do now
And called it a poem,
Our teachers would have given us
Failure notices to take home.

INTERNET HUMOR

Internet and e-mail have revived the sense of humor I thought was lost. Many of the jokes that come in are some I remember from childhood. Others are very sophisticated and thought provoking. Many of them show up in Reader's Digest. Here are just a few I've decided to keep.

IN THE PAST WE DIDN'T APPRAISE MEMORY IN MEGABYTES

In describing the
Idiosyncrasies
Of persons obtuse,
It used to be said
They had a screw loose,
Or were off their rocker
Or weren't all there
Or were out of their tree
or whatever.

Today I'm advised by
Those in the know,

The going appraisal is
He's running a quart low
On the other hand you might opt
For his elevator doesn't
Go clear to the top.

And then there's the one
From the theater bunch,
That simply states
He's out to lunch!

MORE WAYS TO SAY SOMEONE IS STUPID

A few clowns short of a circus
A few fries short of a happy meal
An experiment in Artificial Stupidity
A few beers short of a six-pack
A few peas short of a casserole
Doesn't have all his corn flakes in one box
The wheel's spinning, but the hamster's dead
One Fruit Loop shy of a full bowl.
One taco short of a combination plate
A few feathers short of a whole duck
All foam, no beer
The cheese slid off his cracker
Body by Fisher, Brains by Mattel
Warning: Objects in mirror
are dumber than they appear.
Couldn't pour water out of a boot

with instructions on the heel.
He fell out of the Stupid Tree and
hit every branch on the way down.
As smart as bait
Chimney's clogged
Doesn't have all his dogs on one leash
Forgot to pay his brain bill
Her sewing machine's out of thread
His antenna doesn't pick up all the channels
His belt doesn't go through all the loops
If he had another brain, it would be lonely
Missing a few buttons on his remote control
No grain in the silo
Proof that evolution CAN go in reverse
Receiver is off the hook
Several nuts short of a full pouch
A half bubble off of plumb
Skylight leaks a little
Slinky's kinked
Surfing in Nebraska
Too much yardage between the goal posts
As sharp as a marble

TALE OF TWO POTATOES

You know that all potatoes have eyes. Well, Red Spud and Idaho had eyes for each other and finally got married and had a little one—a real Sweet Potato. They named her "Yam". They wanted the best for little Yam and told her all about the facts of life. They warned her, "Don't go out and get Half Baked because you could get Mashed and get a bad name like Hot Potato and end up with a bunch of Tater Tots".

She said, "Don't worry, no Mr. McSpud will get me into the sack and make a Rotten Potato out of me!" "But" she declared, "I won't stay home and become a Couch Potato either. I will get plenty of food and exercise so I won't be skinny like my Shoestring cousins!"

When she decided to go to Europe, Mr. and Mrs. Potato told her to watch out for the Hard Boiled guys from Ireland, and the greasy guys in France called French Fries. They also said, "If you ever go out West, watch out for the Indians because you could get Scalloped".

She replied, "I will stay on the straight and narrow and not associate with those high class Blue Belles or the ones on the other side of the tracks who advertise their trade on all the trucks with big signs that say 'Frito Lay'."

Mr. and Mrs. Potato wanted the best for Yam, so they sent her to "Idaho P.U." that's Potato University, where the Big Potatoes come from. When she graduated, she'd really be in the Chips.

One day she came home and said "I'm going to marry Walter Cronkite". Mr. and Mrs. Potato were very upset and said, "Oh, no! You can't marry him—he's just a Common Tater!" ***Walter Cronkite is a very popular news commentator.***

BALLOONS

The first balloons I remember were from my Grandpa Gass' store. There were always tears when they broke, but oh what fun we had until that moment. Balloons then were made for children and happy times particularly birthdays. Willard, my little brother used to blow the balloons up, and keep blowing and blowing until they finally burst. Some of them were spectacular, but then he'd cry.

I wonder who invented balloons? And, when? The rubber balloons are pretty much as they always were. You can blow them up until they burst; you can shape them by twisting. We have balloon stores with balloons for all types of people and occasions. Expert balloon entertainers can make animal figures by twisting different shaped balloons together. Our nephew, Don Schilling, also known as D.C. the Clown, is a master of this art as well as many magic tricks.

The foil balloon bouquets, so popular today, last many weeks, but one by one they become tired and each one takes on a separate personality. If they look tired and depressed, let them free in the house. They will follow you from one room to another, hide under chairs and tables, explore closets. When they finally die, lying listless on the floor, bury them in the recycling bin so they can seek a new life.

THE SECRET LIFE OF BALLOONS

By
Don Schilling, aka D.C. the Clown

This is one of the mysteries of the universe, similar to the riddle of the pet rocks that swept the nation a number of years ago.

Balloons are a lot like people. They can be big and round or thin and skinny. Sometimes they are colorful; sometimes drab. They have their ups and downs. If placed under too much stress, they can explode. Some are full of hot air; others get high on helium. It's best to keep the young ones on a short string lest they get into mischief. The older more mature balloons enjoy exploring the world around them. And, like us humans, when they get old, balloons get tired and are easily deflated.

Here is another gem from Don (D.C. the Clown)

A LETTER FROM SANTA CLAUS

HoHoSantaC@northpole.com

Greetings from the North Pole:

I've been very busy, but thought I'd drop you a line along with some helpful holiday ideas (attached file Ho, Ho, Ho Holiday Helpers) which might save you time and money.

Mrs. Claus and I wish you the best this season. The elves and Rudolph also send their regards. My little bunny, Snowflake, is here on my lap, gnawing at the keyboard as I'm typing.

If you haven't written me already as to what you'd like to have for Christmas, you can E-Mail up to 11:45 on Christmas Eve. After that you're out of luck.

Now be good boys and girls and I'll stop by on Christmas Eve to leave you some presents. Please don't leave me any milk and cookies this year. Mrs. Claus (Sarah) has me on a low fat diet. Some celery and carrot sticks with a glass of water will be just fine.

If, however, you want to leave something for the reindeer, they prefer chocolate chip cookies and egg nog.

So, again, be good, love one another and be happy—it's a special form of wisdom.

FAX FROM THE NORTH POLE

Donner and Blitzen have elected to take the early retirement package. This has triggered a good deal of concern about whether they will be replaced, and about other restructuring decisions at the North Pole. The reindeer downsizing was made possible through the purchase of a late model Japanese sled for the CEO's annual trip.

MEDIEVAL WEDDING

September 12th, 1998

All weddings are beautiful and memorable, but this was a most unusual wedding. A strange mixture of the old and new. Because almost a hundred guests were also in costume, it was easy to feel you really were attending a wedding in the 1600's. Only here and there a glimps of something reminded you it really was the 20th century.

We drove many miles north of San Francisco, through beautiful woods on winding roads along rivers and streams. In the mountains on Bohemian Highway, we traveled along the Russian River and through several small villages to reach Duncan Mills where the wedding would be held.

The Inn at Duncan Mills was a colorful, country inn with a large garden. The outdoor wedding chapel was nestled in the woods that surrounded the inn. The garden walls were decorated with many family shields made by the families and friends of the bride and groom. A very large homemade canopy was in place to protect the guests from the bright California sun. This was where our oldest granddaughter, Conni, would be married to Brian.

The ceremony began when the flower girls, Ashley, Amanda and Alesia scattered real rose petals from their baskets. Later, during the ceremony, they passed out bread for the wine and bread-breaking ceremony.

That evening, a big, traditional dinner of roasted game hens, piles of bread, vegetables and vegetable dishes was served. During the meal there was much chatter as all enjoyed the bountiful meal. And then, somebody started to break bread again and the fight was on. All the guests threw chunks of bread at each other. The inn keepers only laughed and said the crows and wild animals would have a feast the next day.

Finally the cutting of the cake brought us back to the 20th century. Each guest was given a tiny bottle of bubbles to blow. The sun picked up many colors in all the thousands of little bubbles floating in the air, and the bride and groom went on their way.

The weather was beautiful and the ceremony touching. It was a memorable occasion to see Brian, Conni and her little girls Ashley and Amanda become a happy family in our modern world..

1999 WAS A YEAR TO REMEMBER First was the surprise party Larry, Bruce and Ron arranged with the help of Shirley Smith and Cecil and Joanne Cushman for their Dad's 80th birthday. Shirley had invited us to dinner at their place and that afternoon she called and said she'd been working in the yard all day and didn't feel like cooking so why didn't we go out. Cecil and Joanne had left on one of their mountain hiking trips. When she picked us up Grayson had a big box of kleenex and I figured his sinus problem was really acting up. We drove out to Charlie's a nice water-view restaurant near the Ferry docks. When we got out of the car, Shirley reminded Grayson to take his kleenex. The waiter led us back to what he said was a nice window table. As we followed the waiter and turned the corner we saw a big table all set for a lot of people and there were the boys and Cecil and Joanne. Grayson handed me the box of kleenex which about that time I really needed.

OUR 60TH ANNIVERSARY PARTY

The open house party at the Senior Center was another spectacular production but not a surprise party. They said they wanted to be sure we would be there. Ron & Vicki, Bruce & Shirley and Larry and Carol with the help of Shirley, Joanne, Carollei and an Honor Student group handled all the food and serving. The party was so beautiful and it was wonderful to see all of our family. Tom, Kathryn's husband was the only one unable to make it. Liam, their 4 year old son charmed everyone. Ashley and Amanda have grown so much in the past few years and helped a lot at the party. Conni and Brian are very happy and he is a wonderful father. Other family guests were our two nieces, Carolyn Baker and Marjorie Schilling, and my cousins Nathalie and Dick Button. Ash's cousin Marian and Owen Alloway, and all of their family—Robin, Guy and Kathy and Keith and Barbara came up from Seattle. Two surprises were a couple from Texas—John and Flo Nix who used to be in the Spinnaker Yacht Club—hadn't seen them for over 20 years, and Larry's godparents Larry &

Barb Kollin from Los Angeles—he fooled us by sending a weird e-mail just as they were leaving for the airport. After reading it, I said to Ash, "Well, I guess Larry and Barb won't be at the party!" I couldn't believe it when we walked into the center and there they were! There was a constant flow of local people to make our celebration complete.

After the party at the center, most of our family went to Walt & Fran's new home (we all call it the Castle) a magnificent mansion a couple of miles from where we live. They sold their Tropic Star Schooner and became landlubbers after living aboard for over 25 years. We spent the evening recovering at home and visiting with Larry & Barb. The family planned the party here in Anacortes so we wouldn't have to travel.

The family was at our house Sunday morning for biscuits and gravy and we visited with all of them. Larry and Carol had already left on their week's trip through the Islands and Canada. It was hard to say good-bye as they left to meet their flight schedules. Ron, Vicki and their gang left Monday morning to pick up Tom in Sacramento and all go on to Disneyland.

Larry and Carol got back from Canada and spent the next week-end with us. On Sunday they went to the Black Powder Shoot with Ward and Jessica, and Monday morning after breakfast here we said good-bye to them. Walt & Fran were gone on a trip but left a key so they could sleep in the Castle. They said it was the fanciest hotel they'd ever slept in.

The following two pieces are what Ash and I wrote to share at the Sixtieth Anniversary party.

A LIFE'S PAINTING

By
Erni Townsend for our
60th Anniversary, September 30, 1999

I watched my Mother start with a blank canvas, and paint a beautiful picture with dabs of colored oils. One of my favorite memories is of her standing on the piano bench and adding just a wee bit of color to a painting on the wall.

We all start life with a blank canvas. The times, and the parents we were born to, the government rules and the geographic location all build the background colors. Every person who enters your life adds dimension and depth to your life's canvas. Every person who touches your life adds a bit of color.

The many bright and sunny colors and vivid memories help us bear the few sad, gray colors. I've seen my Mother change a desert picture into a lake scene with tall pine trees on the hills. Some of the detours in our lives have been like that.

All of our family are an important part of the basic background colors upon which we have built our life's picture. New generations add great depth and soften the loss of loved ones. Our growing family continues to add splashes of color to our lives.

Many have entered our lives over the past 60 years in one place or another, at one time or another. We have been so blessed with many good friends and a fine, wonderful family.

Thank you for helping us celebrate this very special day and adding your bit of color as we continue to paint the picture of our lives.

FRIENDS

by Ash Townsend
September 30, 1999—60th Anniversary

We've been a lot of places
And done a lot of things.
We've seen the Shining Waters
And heard the wind that sings.
We've climbed up on the mountain
Where we could touch the sky,
And what we've done, we've done together,
Together, she and I.

As we traveled down life's highway
With all its hills and bends,
The main thing we've acquired
Is a bunch of damn good friends.
Some count their riches
In terms of silver and gold,
But no financial wealth compares
To friendships new or old.

As newlyweds we were advised
Of consequences dire
If we didn't have at least three kids
Our race would soon expire.
So we set out to do our job
At least give it a try,
And what we did, we did together,
Together, she and I.

We bore three sons—our joy and pride,
And watched them grow up by our side.
As this story nears its ends,
I'm proud to say they're our
Very best friends.

On the 23rd of October 1999, another big event took place when the Seniors marched in a parade to the Center for the Mortgage Burning Ceremony.

CONCLUSION

OCTOBER 10, 2000

Thank you, Kathryn, for inspiring me to write down these stories. Today your grandfather was honored with a laser-carved plaque made of black walnut.

Presented to ASH TOWNSEND
in appreciation of your dedication as
President of the
Anacortes Senior Center Advisory Committee.
1991—2000

The lazer-carved picture of the Fidalgo Center Building is a beautiful example of the world we live in today. It was a great honor to be recognized for all the hard work and long hours he has devoted to seeing that project built and the mortgage burned.

This is the end of "A Century of Stories". For more stories reaching back to 1775; through the 1800's and into the 20th century, read "Other Centuries, Other Stories". Digging back into the history of the 19th and 20th centuries has left me very puzzled. Considering all the detours we have taken, how come all of our family have turned out so good?